Getting Out of B.E.D.

Overcoming Binge-Eating Disorder
One Day at a Time

Megan R. Bartlett

Copyright © 2008 by Megan R. Bartlett

ISBN 0-7414-4329-5

Published by:

INFIꝏITY
PUBLISHING.COM

1094 New DeHaven Street, Suite 100
West Conshohocken, PA 19428-2713
Info@buybooksontheweb.com
www.buybooksontheweb.com
Toll-free (877) BUY BOOK
Local Phone (610) 941-9999
Fax (610) 941-9959

Printed in the United States of America

Printed on Recycled Paper

Published January 2008

Acknowledgments

I would like to gratefully acknowledge all those who helped make this book possible: Pat Casinelli, L.C.S.W. who was instrumental during my first attempts to overcome binge eating; Thom Rutledge, L.C.S.W. for his endorsement of this book and for sharing with me what someone once told him: "someone out there wants to hear what you have to say in the way that you have to say it"; Robert F. Bornstein, Ph.D. and Megan MacCausland for their helpful advice about the organization and structure of early versions of the book; Isaac Williams for designing the book's cover; Jonathan Canady for designing the inside cover art and for creating my website; Rachel Dumont for reading through and commenting on later drafts; everyone who courageously shared a personal story about getting out of B.E.D.; and of course, Mom, Dad, Colin, Angie, Isaac, Becky, Jen and Trish for their endless support and love.

Introduction

from Blues at Dawn

I don't dare remember in the morning
Don't dare remember in the morning.
If I recall the day before,
I wouldn't get up no more—
So I don't dare remember in the morning.

--Robert Frost

Suffocating and barely hiding it, I had held my breath under the blankets for so long, ever trying to create the illusion of serenity, but I knew I couldn't last much longer. I was panic-stricken at the thought of what everyone would think of me when I inevitably began thrashing around under the covers, gasping for air. One day, though, the alarm clock resounded, waking me up to the realization that I had a choice: stay cocooned in bed or stand up and get moving. Though it was at one time a safe haven, my bed had grown increasingly nightmarish, which made my decision that day an easy one. I saw with crystal clarity that progress and life itself would be hindered until I threw off the covers and swung my feet over the side of the bed. My only worry was whether I would be able to make the same decision again at the dawn of the next day.

Trying to overcome Binge-Eating Disorder (B.E.D.) is a lot like deciding whether or not to get out of bed each day. Time and again, I must choose between staying in B.E.D., essentially putting my life on hold, and getting out of B.E.D. to progress forward in life. The choice is mine and there are, indeed, days when I choose to stay in B.E.D. On those days, the familiar comforts of my security blankets (food and bingeing) make my B.E.D. seem like a warm and inviting place. I convince myself that the temporary relief from my anxiety, over-excitement, depression, loneliness, or boredom is worth the potential lack of progress that day. Yet, if I stay in B.E.D. too long, the blankets which were once comfortable begin to get tangled around me, choking me once again with feelings of shame, disgust, and self-loathing. As exhausting as it is to throw off those covers, I must remind myself that it is well

1

worth it to do so at any point in the day. I can then stand up and walk away from my B.E.D. for as long as I choose.

Throwing off those covers is so empowering, although in the early days of my recovery, I was satisfied just to pull them down from over my head. I'd tell myself, "I will go one day without bingeing." When I succeeded, I felt on top of the world. The more times I nudged those blankets away from me, the stronger I felt. When the stresses of life closed in on me and I found myself clinging to my blankets again, I resolved to turn to a self-help program and my counselor. I delved into the reasons why I kept returning to my old ways and saw more clearly that my blankets were preventing me from living the life I wanted to live.

Over three years into my recovery, I feel stronger and more confident than ever. I won't claim that I emerge from beneath the covers and walk away from my B.E.D. every single day, but I'm aware that I have the option to do so. I know that if I choose not to, I'm essentially hitting the snooze button and putting my life on hold. Fortunately, after a day or two of laying in B.E.D., I start to remember how nice it is to be out of it. I don't spend hours each day counting calories, obsessing over the number I saw on my scale that morning, or agonizing over what I should and should not eat. I'm gentler on myself. I have more space in my head to think about my family and friends. I'm able to make short term goals and see them through. Just getting out of B.E.D. that first time revealed much of what I had been missing.

If you've been in B.E.D. wrestling, as I was, with covers which once provided peace and security, *Getting Out of B.E.D.* may provide you with the encouragement to push them aside. There are so many wonderful possibilities; not bingeing and obsessing about food are just two of the more obvious ones. Just think of how great it would feel to be free from the terrifying grip of the bathroom scale or to go to a restaurant without worrying that what you eat will later trigger a binge. You may even find, like I did, that you now have the mental and emotional space to tackle some long-term goals like going back to school, revising your résumé, or buying a house. Many doors are waiting to be opened by you. Getting out of B.E.D. is the first step.

Chapter One: When Food Becomes Enemy #1

> "…food is the vital way we celebrate anything that matters—
> a birthday, a new job, an anniversary; it's how we mark the connections
> between us, how we celebrate life." [1]

> -- Nigella Lawson

The above quote calls to mind wonderful images of close friends, laughter, and good times. Yet for those of us who suffer from an eating disorder, food brings anything but happiness; meal times and social events are often associated with anxiety, anger, depression, or guilt. We may obsess over what we should and should not eat, how many calories we consume, and what people are thinking when they see us eat certain foods. No longer is food an enjoyable part of a gathering; it is a feared and reviled nemesis.

I have spent over fifteen years battling Enemy #1. Three years ago, in an effort to bring about a change, I chose to stop fighting and start trying to understand when and why food had become my enemy. A year later, I began writing this book. As I talked with others about my experiences with Binge-Eating Disorder, I discovered two important things: 1) many people had never heard of the disorder, thus filling me with an urgent need to discuss it and 2) several of my close friends and co-workers were also stuck in B.E.D. A few even agreed to share their stories for this book.

The first person I spoke with was a young woman who I'll call "Amy". She was one of my co-workers and we frequently ate lunch together. During one lunch she said she had eaten too much ice cream the night before and had since vowed that she would not eat ice cream again for a "long time." I heard similarities between her words and my own thoughts about food, desiring it one minute and hating it the next. I wondered whether she, too, might be prone to bingeing. I decided to tell Amy about my eating disorder and confessed to her that I had been wondering whether she ever experienced anything similar. She said she had and she was eager to tell me more…

---

[1] Lawson, Nigella. (2004). *Feast: Food That Celebrates Life*. New York: Hyperion. p. vii (Reprinted by permission).

Amy's Story

As a kid I was really picky and I wouldn't eat anything. I just didn't like a lot of stuff. Sometimes I'd have to sit at the dinner table until I ate something. I was really small and my parents were always trying to get me to eat more. So I constantly had this idea in my mind: "I am really skinny and I eat like a bird." And then when I got to be a teenager, I started eating more but I still thought of myself as really skinny. I ate whatever I wanted and didn't gain weight. When I was in college I thought the same thing and ate whatever I wanted. Then one year I gained twenty pounds and I didn't understand it because I had always been "the skinniest, littlest kid" and suddenly I thought, "God, this just isn't me." At that point I had an image of myself as a "fat person" and it was the opposite of the way I thought others wanted me to be. Nowadays, I fluctuate. If I've lost weight I think, "Oh, I'm skinny. I can eat whatever I want. That was just a fluke." And then I'll eat a lot and gain weight and think, "I'm not skinny. I'm doomed to always be fat." So, how I see myself really changes from day to day.

When I think about it now I can see that my bingeing started in college because you have every possible food there is. People would eat huge trays full of food. You would just get one thing after another because your friends would keep coming in [to the cafeteria] and you'd want to get the most from your meal plan. And you couldn't control what was there. Everything was there. So, I gained a lot of weight--twenty pounds or so--and I wanted to lose it so I joined Weight Watchers®.

With Weight Watchers® there are points; different foods are worth different points and you have a range of points each day. If you eat within the range you'll lose weight. It does help you eat healthier but it also can get kind of obsessive. I would plan out my points, but it was almost like planning them and knowing what I was going to eat made me want to eat more. It made me constantly think about food. And it was always a battle to not eat. I would think, "Why is this so hard? All I have to do to lose weight is not eat." Not eating the things I loved just made me want them more. So, every time I would find something that was low in points like a low-calorie food or dessert that wasn't too bad for me, I would not be able to stop myself. I would have one and then I'd have to have

4

another and another until I ate so much of it that I felt horrible about myself. But I couldn't stop myself. I'd think, "Well, I've already eaten this much I might as well just finish it." Giving in to the urge initially felt good; I wanted the food and knew that because I couldn't have it, I would feel anxious about it and obsessed with it. If I just ate it I would feel better. Sometimes, though, I'd force myself to stop eating something I felt anxious about by throwing whatever was left of it into the trash and pouring water on it. That was the only way to be sure I wouldn't pull it out of the trash later and try to finish it.

When I started trying to break out of this cycle, I was reminded of one of the things that they told us at Weight Watchers®. They said when you're first trying to lose weight or eat healthier you have to control your environment and what food is in it because it's too hard to control yourself. So the idea is if you can't trust yourself around a particular food then you have to just not buy it. I know I can't control myself around certain foods so I can't have them in the house.

For example, the other night I bought ice cream sandwiches. I thought, "I haven't had ice cream sandwiches in so long. I'll get some for dessert." They come in a pack of ten and my roommate ate some but then one night I just got in "binge mode". I don't know why it was. I ate dinner and then I thought, "All right. I'll have an ice cream sandwich." So I had one. And then immediately after I finished it I thought, "I have to have another." So I had another. And luckily that was the last one in the box. But then I thought, "I have to have cereal." So I had a bowl of cereal. And I ended up eating so much more than I needed, but it was like something in me had to do it and I wasn't going to stop until that urge was satisfied. So there are still lots of things which trigger a binge. I just have to never buy them.

There are a few foods I try to substitute for my binge triggers; for me frozen grapes are really good at helping me when I want to eat ice cream; they have the same consistency. When I eat them, I don't crave ice cream anymore. For a lot of foods there are no substitutes; I'll want to eat it anyway. Those are the things that are really off-limits. That really does help me. It's not a long list of foods, so I don't think it's detrimental. Another thing that's helped me is that I learned to think about food differently. At a place like [the office] where junk food is constantly available it's easy to think, "Well, it's free. Why not eat it?" I had to start thinking about it in terms of, "Well, it's free money-wise, but it's not free points-wise or in terms of feeling good about myself."

It's hard to know if I'll ever be free from bingeing altogether. It's kinda like a self-perpetuating cycle; when I feel really fat I'm more likely to eat more and when I feel skinny I'm likely to not eat as much. This keeps me whatever weight I am. When I was running a lot, I was definitely feeling skinnier and probably was skinnier. I didn't obsess about my body or my weight as much and I didn't think about food as much. But whenever I start to feel fat, it's all I can think about. My bingeing is definitely less frequent in the last couple years, but I always wonder if I'll go back to how I used to be. I really don't know.

Chapter Two: What is Binge-Eating Disorder?

If you've ever been stuck in B.E.D. or known someone who has, some of Amy's story may sound familiar—the obsessive thoughts about body image and weight, the food cravings and avoidance, and the feeling of being out of control. These are all common characteristics of Binge-Eating Disorder and they each play a role in what's often called "the binge cycle". Dr. Joyce D. Nash, author of *Binge No More: Your Guide to Overcoming Disordered Eating*, talks of "the ABC model of behavior. *Antecedents*, or the "A" part of the model, are the events that come first and, together or singly, trigger the behavior. The binge is the behavior in question and is the "B" part of the model. The consequences, or "C", follow the behavior, and are the events that serve to reinforce "B"—that is, make it more or less likely that the behavior will happen again."[2]

For Amy, the "A" of the model was the thought that she, who had once been thin, was now a "fat person". The "B" was her bingeing. The consequences of that bingeing, the "C", were guilty feelings (and at times, a temporary relief from tension). The result of dieting or restricting calories may be physical hunger or a craving for foods not eaten. If we're not aware of the triggers and results of our behaviors, we may become trapped in a "self-perpetuating cycle", as witnessed previously through Amy, in which our feelings or thoughts seemingly control our behavior.

Before we can take steps to break that cycle, it may be helpful to understand what defines Binge-Eating Disorder and then assess our own thoughts about food and feelings about ourselves in order to gain a better understanding of their impact on our eating habits.

The American Psychiatric Association's *Diagnostic and Statistical Manual of Mental Disorders, Fourth Edition*[3] is a diagnostic tool used by mental health professionals such as

---

[2] Nash, Joyce D. (1999). *Binge No More: Your Guide to Overcoming Disordered Eating*. Oakland: New Harbinger Publications, Inc. pp.109 (Reprinted by permission).
[3] American Psychiatric Association: *Diagnostic and Statistical Manual of Mental Disorders,* Fourth Edition. Washington, DC, American Psychiatric Association, 1994 (Reprinted by permission).

psychiatrists, psychologists, counselors, and social workers. The following is the definition of a binge and a description of the characteristics, frequency, and prevalence of Binge-Eating Disorder[4] according to that book:

Definition of a binge:

> "A binge is defined as eating in a discrete period of time an amount of food that is definitely larger than most individuals would eat under similar circumstances" (p. 545).

Characteristics of Binge-Eating Disorder:

> "...recurrent episodes of binge eating associated with subjective and behavioral indicators of impaired control over, and significant distress about, the binge eating and the absence of the regular use of inappropriate compensatory behaviors (such as self-induced vomiting, misuse of laxatives and other medications, fasting, and excessive exercise) that are characteristic of Bulimia Nervosa" (p. 729).

Indicators of impaired control:

> "...eating very rapidly, eating until feeling uncomfortably full, eating large amounts of food when not hungry, eating alone because of embarrassment over how much one is eating, and feeling disgust, guilt, or depression after overeating" (p. 729).

Frequency of binges:

> "Binge episodes must occur, on average, at least 2 days a week for a period of at least 6 months" (p. 730).

Prevalence:

> "In samples drawn from weight-control programs, the overall prevalence varies from approximately 15% to 50% (with a mean of 30%), with females approximately 1.5 times more likely to have this eating pattern than males. In

---

[4] It is debated whether the terms "Binge-Eating Disorder" and "Compulsive Overeating" are interchangeable. Since the American Psychiatric Association uses the term "Binge-Eating Disorder", I will do the same throughout this book.

nonpatient community samples, a prevalence rate of 0.7%-4% has been reported" (p. 730).

Incidence of Obesity in Binge-Eating Disorder:

"Individuals with this eating pattern seen in clinical settings have varying degrees of obesity...In weight-control clinics, individuals with this eating pattern are, on average, more obese and have a history of more marked weight fluctuations than individuals without this pattern. In nonpatient community samples, most individuals with this eating pattern are overweight (although some have never been overweight)" (p. 730).

Although not intended as a substitute for professional evaluation, you may find it helpful to complete the following Risk Assessment for Binge Eating. I designed it and wrote the questions based on the three main components of the binge cycle: 1) obsessive/intrusive thoughts about food, weight, and body image; 2) behaviors related to eating, dieting, and bingeing; and 3) feelings/emotions related to self-worth, self-esteem, and self-image. As you answer each question, be honest with yourself. Yes, it can be difficult to admit that you think about food 16 of your 17 waking hours each day. You may feel ashamed to note that you're not in control of your eating. But an accurate assessment of where you are right now will give you an idea of what areas need special attention. You may even decide to photocopy these pages and fill them out once a month to track your progress over time.

Risk Assessment for Binge Eating

Please read the following statements and circle a number, depending on how much each statement pertains to you.

> 1 = definitely FALSE
>
> 2 = FALSE, for the most part
>
> 3 = neither FALSE, nor TRUE
>
> 4 = TRUE, for the most part
>
> 5 = definitely TRUE

1. I think about food and/or eating before, during, and after meals.

   1   2   3   4   5

2. If I eat what I consider to be "too much", I attempt to restrict my calories or go on a diet the next day.

   1   2   3   4   5

3. I worry about how much exercise I get each day.

   1   2   3   4   5

4. I feel utterly helpless to control my eating.

   1   2   3   4   5

5. Each morning, I think, "Today I will eat better than yesterday."

   1   2   3   4   5

6. I prefer to eat alone than with friends, co-workers, or family.

   1   2   3   4   5

7. I am rarely satisfied with myself.

   1   2   3   4   5

8. When I'm out in public, I feel as though people are staring at me.

   1   2   3   4   5

9. I regularly avoid certain foods that I consider "bad" for me.

   1   2   3   4   5

10. I binge at least twice a week every week.

    1   2   3   4   5

11. When I weigh myself, the number I see on the scale affects how I feel about myself.

    1   2   3   4   5

12. Most days, I worry about what I should or should not eat.

    1   2   3   4   5

13. I often eat when I am bored, lonely, depressed, and/or "stressed out".

    1   2   3   4   5

14. I often think, "I am fat."

    1   2   3   4   5

15. If I binge, I feel like a failure.

    1   2   3   4   5

16. The negative way I perceive myself detracts from my relationships with others.

    1   2   3   4   5

17. During a typical binge, I eat so much that I feel physically uncomfortable, sometimes even to the point of wanting to throw up.

    1   2   3   4   5

18. During a binge I am emotionally numb.

    1   2   3   4   5

19. I worry about what others think of me when they see me eat.

    1   2   3   4   5

20. I weigh myself more than once a week.

    1   2   3   4   5

21. Only those who are thin and/or attractive deserve to be happy.

    1   2   3   4   5

22. Sometimes I think everything would be better if I could just lose some weight.

    1   2   3   4   5

23. After a binge I am disgusted with myself.

    1   2   3   4   5

24. I scrutinize myself in the mirror at least five times a day or I consciously avoid mirrors altogether.

    1   2   3   4   5

25. When I eat, I'm afraid I won't be able to stop.

    1   2   3   4   5

26. I avoid going to restaurants and/or parties so I don't have to be seen eating in public.

    1   2   3   4   5

27. If I eat something that I consider to be "unhealthy", I feel guilty.

    1   2   3   4   5

28. I feel depressed much of the time.

    1   2   3   4   5

29. When I binge, I eat many of the things that I don't usually allow myself to eat.

  1   2   3   4   5

30. I doubt I can achieve any of my goals.

  1   2   3   4   5

Now that you're done, add together all the circled numbers to determine your score. (Scores will range between 30 and 150.) Higher numbers indicate greater concern with food, weight, and body image, which may translate into a higher risk for developing B.E.D.

After reading the description of Binge-Eating Disorder and filling out the assessment, you may be thinking, "I had no idea I thought about food that much." If so, don't panic. Often times, just being aware that we're trapped in B.E.D. is incentive enough to decide to get out of it. Others of you may feel like you haven't learned anything you didn't already know about yourself. Even so, you now have a starting point from which to assess your progress. A year from now you may look back at your answers and think, "I've come a long way!" Some among you may have had a low score on the questionnaire but thought of someone you know who may have trouble with binge eating. If so, please read on. This book is intended for concerned friends and family as well as for those of us still in B.E.D. Indeed, part of my motivation for this book was to convey to those who do not have an eating disorder what it's like to live in the confines of one. For me, B.E.D. was not stifling at first; it only gradually began to threaten my well-being. My experiences with B.E.D. commence with "Wheel of Fortune".

Chapter Three: In B.E.D. for Many Years

from #<u>875</u>

I stepped from Plank to Plank
A slow and cautious way
The Stars about my Head I felt
About my Feet the Sea.

I knew not but the next
Would be my final inch—
This gave me that precarious Gait
Some call Experience.

--Emily Dickinson

How did I get in B.E.D. in the first place?

As an early teen, I left the dinner table feeling full, yet already looking forward to "snack time." Around 7:30 every night, if our homework was done (and mine rarely wasn't), my brother and I would settle down in front of the TV to watch "Wheel of Fortune", each of us with a bowl of three cookies (or some other proportionately sized snack) to munch on. Although I always tried to make my cookies last as long as possible, when they were gone, I'd glance longingly at my brother's remaining pile. I'd think, "How can he not have eaten them yet? Maybe he doesn't want them." Out of a desire to eat more but not be seen doing so, I devised various schemes to convince him to give me one of his cookies.

When he was young and extremely impressionable, I'd play mind games with him, pretending I was getting sick. I'd moan and groan, hold my stomach, and say something melodramatic like, "Pleeeease can I have one of your cookies? I'll *die* if you don't give me one." (He nearly always handed one over in order to "save" his big sis, although nowadays he claims to have always known I was faking it!) Other times, I'd just wait and hope that he'd get up and leave the room (or if I was particularly impatient, I'd send him out of the room on a "mission" for me) so I could steal a bite—enough so that I could taste it but not so much that he would notice the missing piece. (Although a few times I stole a whole cookie and was then forced to vehemently deny that I did:

"I did NOT eat one of your cookies! You must have eaten it yourself.")

At some point, it dawned on me that I could eat more than just a crumb of my brother's cookies. But it wouldn't be easy. I would have to walk upstairs, enter the kitchen, open the pantry and the cookie bag, grab few enough cookies so that they wouldn't appear to be missing, close the cookie bag and pantry, sneak out of the kitchen and back downstairs, eat the cookies before entering the TV room and get back into my place in front of the TV without being noticed. Such feats seemed particularly bold to someone like me, who rarely disobeyed her parents. It sure would have been easier to just ask my mom and dad for some extra cookies, but I was trying to respect the "only 3 cookies" rule. I also knew that if I could pull off my "cookie theft", my parents would continue to think I was an angel and I would get to eat more of the tasty foods I loved.

On certain nights, I convinced myself I not only *wanted* more cookies, I *needed* more cookies. I tuned out from the TV set and set my own wheel of fortune in motion, beginning with a mental pep talk ("You can do it, Meg. No sweat."), followed by a quick jog up the stairs from the basement. With heightened senses, I strained at the door to the kitchen to hear my parents' voices. My only hope of pulling this off was if they were in one of the bedrooms, the bathroom, or outside. When I was sure the coast was clear, I opened the door and tiptoed to the pantry. Scarcely breathing for fear of alerting someone to my presence, I grabbed the cool pantry doorknob, which felt clammy in my sweaty palms. I turned the knob carefully, opened the door slowly, and took a deep breath.

This was the hardest part: getting the cookie bag open without making it rustle. It seemed impossible! My first attempt yielded an audible "CRK!" which made me flush beet red and pause to listen for approaching feet. After the second "CRK!" my heart was in my throat and I contemplated aborting the mission. I heard voices having it out with each other in my head: "Megan, you don't need to eat more cookies. Close the door and go back to the TV." "Megan! You're just seconds away from eating more cookies. You can do it!" The cookie thief's voice won. I exhaled quietly and breathed again. Without another thought, I maneuvered my finger under the edge of the bag and lifted the top lip. Now to pull out the plastic tray into which all those delicious morsels were tucked. One last "RUSTLE" and the bag was open a crack! I dared not try to open it further, so I deftly extended my index and middle fingers into the tray and smiled as my fingers brushed against a "Soft Batch" chocolate chip cookie. I slipped it out of its tray, popping it in my mouth right away ("Why risk not being able to eat any if someone walks in on you?", chimed in the cookie thief). The second cookie, I placed gingerly on the shelf while I held my breath and closed up the cookie bag. Mission almost accomplished! I grabbed the cookie, tossed it in my mouth, brushed the crumbs off the shelf lest anyone notice and closed the pantry door with two hands so as not to make a peep. I spun on my bare feet, leapt down the stairs like a gazelle, stopping just before the closed door to the TV room to compose myself, and then entered. "Hi," I said to my brother as nonchalantly as possible while the words "I did it!" ran through my head over and over like a scrolling neon sign. Successfully nabbing a cookie or two was a bit like tossing another cover on the bed on a cold winter's night— it felt *really* good.

I engaged in such scheming and deceit not because I had a penchant for trickery or an evil streak, but because a large part of me worried what my brother or parents would think if I simply asked for another cookie. Even at the tender young age of twelve, I was terrified of disappointing others—especially my parents. Without them ever explicitly telling me to work hard and aim high, I did so. I was a "high-achiever"—your classic first-born child. I took on responsibilities without being asked. I set goals for myself and made sure I accomplished them. Throughout my teenage years I did my homework on time, practiced flute and piano regularly and never stayed out past my curfew. I craved a structured and organized life—in and out of school. In fact, I never wanted to do anything that might upset the balance of my world. Little did I know, this very desire for control and balance was leading me towards an unstable relationship with food.

By the time I was in ninth grade, what I ate or didn't eat, how much I weighed, and what I looked like were almost all I could think about. One morning before gym class, I listened intently as my friend gave me diet and exercise tips in case I wanted to tone up my "love handles". Seeing her as an attractive, popular, and *thin* girl, and desperately wanting to be well-liked, I followed her advice. (After all, I believed that she was popular *because* she was thin.) I grew more mindful of what I ate, counting calories and forbidding myself to eat certain foods. For two or three days I could eat "well" and feel good about myself. Eating well made me feel like I was in control of things; there was no way I'd get fat as long as I ate well. For a few days at a time, I could convince myself that I didn't even want cake, cookies, or candy. When confronted with such foods, I'd tell myself, "It's bad for you. Why would you want to eat something bad?" And so I'd survive for a few days without these treats until I ultimately "caved" and ate something I thought I shouldn't. The first few bites were easy to rationalize: "I earned it for being so good these past few days." Minutes later, however, I'd begin to feel ashamed, guilty, and mad at myself. In that state of mind, I turned to bingeing. It was both a punishment for having taken that first mouthful (which seemed like "the beginning of the end") and also a way of packing in whatever I wanted because the next day I was going to "start over" with the calorie counting and food avoidance. ("And this time," I told myself, "I'll be really good!")

Despite my best attempts, staying away from certain foods was not easy. One of my favorite desserts was yellow cake with vanilla butter-cream frosting. It had long ago been relegated to the "forbidden list", that ever-growing inventory of tasty, but fattening treats I knew I had to avoid if I wanted to stay thin. During the two weeks immediately after my high school graduation, I attended close to a dozen parties and was confronted at each one with a colorfully frosted sheet cake. At the first party, the unusual red and black icing (our school colors) called out to me: "Don't you wanna know what *black* icing tastes like?!" After one taste, I knew it was just like all the other colors of icing, sweet and delicious, but with the peculiar side effect of discoloring my tongue and lips. In preparation for the next party I told myself I wouldn't eat any cake because the icing would stain my mouth. I entered the room, saw the two tables full of food and my eyes scanned over everything, searching for the cake. There it was—in all its *white and green* glory. "White and green?! Ah, yes. Our senior class colors. I wonder what *green* icing tastes like. Surely it won't stain my mouth like black icing does."

At my own party that weekend I allowed myself to have a piece of cake while a rousing chorus of "It's my party and I'll eat if I want to…" ran through my head. Later that night, however, the music stopped. With all the guests gone and no one to distract me from my guilt, I berated myself for having eaten something with "absolutely no nutritional value". I felt certain that the next piece of cake would make my stomach instantly jiggly, much like the effect of a cold fridge on liquid Jell-O gelatin. I silently vowed to leave the next party before they cut the cake just so I wouldn't be tempted. But before I knew it, I was reaching for my own little square of perfectly iced yellow cake and telling myself like a smoker trying to quit cold turkey, "This is really the last time." Two weeks and four more parties later, I had eaten cake at every event and was convinced that in doing so I had lost complete control over my eating. I was doomed to be fat.

Once the party season was over, I swore I'd "never eat cake again". That promise lasted for about three days until I discovered that much of my own leftover graduation cake was wrapped up in easily accessible single portions in our deep freezer downstairs. I started playing games again, challenging myself to remove a piece of cake from the freezer without making a sound, expose it from within its aluminum foil hiding place, and eat it *frozen* before my parents came downstairs. There was probably little risk of them walking in on me, but I felt an adrenaline rush none-the-less, similar to the way I felt as a young girl stealing cookies from the pantry. This "cake walk" went on every day for a week until I had eaten nearly half of what was in the freezer and was truly sick of cake. What had started in ninth grade as a self-imposed diet and exercise challenge was rapidly developing into a much greater obstacle.

*   *   *   *   *

A decade later, when I began reviewing my past in search of reasons why food had such a stronghold on my life, I couldn't help but think of my father, whose eating habits were parallel to my own. He grew up in a home in which there was always plenty to eat and the idea of overeating was unheard of. As an adult, he continued to binge. I witnessed this behavior and came to model my habits in a similar fashion. He often ate in secret, "grazing" for food between meals and looking guilty if caught. Likewise if I didn't want to be seen overeating, I had two choices: don't eat at all except at mealtimes or eat in secret and hope I don't get caught.

The latter was the less disagreeable of the two options and it seemed to work for my dad most of the time, so I, too, learned to "sneak" food when others weren't looking.

This deception led to a lot of shame and guilt. I sensed that shame in my dad, too. As a Lutheran pastor he spends much of his time in front of a large group of people, which I imagine could be both empowering and frightening. When I was twelve, I remember his first Sunday at our new church. He introduced himself to the congregation with a joke about his baldness and his weight. I felt sad that he would put himself down like that and wondered why he was ashamed of himself. How could such a great man be so quick to demean himself? The question resurfaced in my mind over the years. My dad's negative view of himself contradicted his true identity. When I wrote this chapter, I had the opportunity to tell him how I felt that day. He said, "That's funny 'cause I never would have thought of that…to me it was kind of just acknowledging who I am, like acknowledging my baldness. But maybe it was a way of getting that out in the public so that people would simply say, 'Okay, here's a fat pastor.' And they wouldn't challenge me on anything; they wouldn't think twice when they saw me eat seconds or thirds."

Recently I had the opportunity to see my dad introduce himself to another new congregation. His words were reminiscent of that day almost eighteen years ago. "Please join us in the fellowship hall after worship for refreshments, something near and dear to my heart…and stomach," he said while patting his gut. He got a chuckle out of the congregation and I smiled, too, but felt a twinge of sadness. Some months prior to this event, I felt as though I needed to know more about where his disordered eating came from. I wanted to know more about how his upbringing shaped his eating habits in order to piece together the development of my own.

We met at my apartment one evening. I had agonized for a few days prior about what to make for dinner. "Burgers? Nah, not my specialty. Roast chicken? Nah, too formal. What about pasta?" I wondered whether my dad, like me, had ever counted calories and if pasta was one of those binge-trigger foods for him as it was for me at one time. I emailed him to ask if pasta would be okay and he said, "Pasta would be great!" So, we sat down that night over a home-cooked meal of pasta, garlic bread and a salad. I was never so aware in my whole life of the irony of my troubles with food. I was terrified of being perceived as eating too much in front of others, yet desirous of close relationships with family and friends. All my life, connecting with loved ones has involved food. Whether gabbing with childhood friends as we walked to the local store for candy or meeting with college friends for a cappuccino, there weren't many times when I had the opportunity to relate to others without "the food factor". And there I was that night with my dad, sharing a meal and dessert with him before talking about our shared eating disorder.

After the meal, I grabbed my notes and mini tape recorder and asked my first question: "How big a role did food play in your childhood?" He responded without hesitation:

Food was a major event as I was growing up. My dad's favorite mealtime phrase was, "It's better to bust your bellies than to let good vittles go to waste." So we never wasted anything. I think that comes from people who've lived through the Depression. At mealtimes, seconds and thirds were always encouraged. Lunch and supper always had to have a dessert of some kind. We always had candy dishes out with candy in them and there was more in the buffet drawer so that when that was empty you could fill it up again. At holidays you would keep all the food out and pick at it constantly. I guess that's common for a lot of Americans but in my house there was so much food it was ridiculous. There was never a sense as I grew up that you could ever eat too much. You just ate until you "bust your bellies". Full was normal. Full was the desired effect for a meal.

Because there was plenty of food in our house, I ate whenever I wanted to. My dad was on the road a lot for work and my mom used to work three to eleven so I was left on my own during my teenage years. My brother and sister had left the house by then. I got to raise myself, which was scary and neat at the same time. I learned to cook which was a good thing but since we had snacks all the time, I turned to food whenever I was hungry, bored, nervous, or stressed out.

I went into college weighing 185 and came out of college weighing at least 210. The "freshman fifteen" was real for me. By the end of the first year, I had certainly met my future wife, your mom. And we came to a very good understanding: she would eat my vegetables and I would eat her meat. We shared all meals together and if she got a dessert she didn't want then I could eat that too...on top of my own. So that was great. I enjoyed meals in college. I just ate a lot. My roommate would bring back tins of chocolate chip cookies from his mom and no matter where he hid them in that small dorm room, I'd find them and eat them even though they weren't mine. One time he and his fiancée invited me and your mom over for a dinner party where they were having baked chicken. At the end of the meal, there was still meat left on the leg of her chicken and I said, "Can I finish that?" And everybody was aghast as I ate what was left of her chicken. I didn't even think anything of it. It was just "Well, there's something left on there. You don't let food go to waste."

After college, when I realized I was way too chubby, I weighed myself every day. That's what my parents did for years and years. It wasn't until recently, when I read a book on overcoming binge eating, that I thought it was even a possibility not to weigh every day. I just thought, "Well, how will I know how much I weigh today if I don't weigh myself?" As I continued to record my weight, I tried to cut back on sweets when I weighed too much. In fact, there was one point at which I challenged the church congregation where I worked to help me lose weight. Depending on how many pounds I lost, they would donate money to a charity. I probably lost fifteen or twenty pounds, but I put it right back on. I started to learn what was healthy eating but just because I knew it didn't mean I would do it.

I still continued to binge and I tried to hide it from others. I didn't want people to know how much I was eating. If I went down to the bakery to get donuts I'd think, "All right, now how many will your mom think that I bought? If I buy half a dozen and I cram three into my mouth before I get home, then I'll tell her I bought four and I brought three home. And then I can still have another one and she'll get two." There was always an element of sneakiness to it. Part of that sneakiness was shame, but it was also just the thrill of trying to get away with it. I mean if your mom bought ice cream and I was able to open up the ice cream, shave off the top eighth to a quarter of an inch and put the lid back and her not suspect that I had done that, there was some kind of thrill of accomplishment. If I could open a package of cookies, and take two out, so there's still the same number of cookies in each tray, and seal it back up, that was good.

One of the reasons I kept bingeing was just the availability of food. It was so frustrating working from home because every place you went in the house, you had to pass the pantry. No matter what, my hand would just go to the doorknob and I would find something to eat. I couldn't open the pantry without eating something. Crackers, cookies, pretzels, or open the refrigerator and eat some cheese. I was always, all day long, eating something. Today, I'll binge on candy, cake, cookies...usually sweets, but even if there's leftover cold spaghetti in the fridge, I'll certainly eat that. I'm even famous for eating frozen cookies that your mom has hidden in the freezer. Six weeks ago I walked past a trashcan at work and saw that somebody had thrown out a box of leftover donut holes. I went through the trashcan and pulled out donut holes that looked okay. And it was then that I thought, "Paul. You've got a problem if you're going through the trash...dumpster-diving." It wasn't that I was hungry or my stomach was going to burst if I didn't have something to eat right then. It was just there.

Even when food isn't readily available, I'll stop somewhere to get some. I'll go in with the intention of getting a small size ice cream or milkshake and then come out with a medium and say, "Well, at least I didn't get the large. I must be a good guy 'cause I didn't get the large." But another part of me feels awful. The thing that gets me so mad with binge eating is that after I eat something I beat up on myself. I think, "Why did you do that? You didn't have to have that ice cream. You didn't have to have that Frosty. You could have driven past." And then I think I'm a bad person. I hate that. I hate that feeling. I do well for a while and then I have a relapse. You might think it would be very simple to just stop this kind of behavior and lose some weight. But it's not simple! It's so frustrating.

One thing that helps with the bingeing is to eat regularly throughout the day. I consistently eat breakfast at 5:30am, a small snack at 9:30-10 o'clock, a relatively minimal lunch at noon, a mid-afternoon snack, supper around five, and then a snack around 8:30 or 9pm. It's the snacks that can go higher or lower. If my brain is in gear, I measure out my snacks. I'll only get out a few crackers. I'll only get out four or five pretzels rather than bring the whole bowl or the whole bag or whole box to where I am. One of the things that I would like to start doing at evening meals is serve myself a plateful and then don't bring the rest of the food over to the table. It's tough to have bowls of leftover food on the table in front of me 'cause I just want to keep on eating.

Today, whenever I do binge, I resolve to be better. "I won't do that again. I'll be a better person." Of course, by ourselves that can't happen; this is why there are Overeaters Anonymous groups. We can't do it by ourselves. I rely on God, as well as my counselor and self-help books. I can't do this alone.

*   *   *   *   *

Although most of us with an eating disorder "resolve to be better", we must realize that very often our human resolve isn't enough. My dad's continued faith in God's love and goodness motivates him to overcome his daily temptations to stay in B.E.D. I, too, hope for a "total recovery" through faith with the aid of daily prayer and bible study. Faith in an all-powerful, loving God who has a plan and purpose for my life has had a profound impact on my eating habits. When I feel the urge to binge I can turn to God in prayer and ask him to take away the urge. I can leave the kitchen area and read certain Bible passages that are inspiring to me. If I do succumb to a binge, I can still feel confident that I'm not a bad person because of it; my position as a child of God has not changed just because I binged. This knowledge carries over to other roles I play and continues to serve as a healthy reminder if I do binge. I'm still a loving daughter, sister, and friend. I'm still a responsible and competent worker. I'm still a lover of music and poetry. I'm still a person who cares about the earth and all therein. I'm still all of these things even when my will to avoid a binge is weakened.

"So," you may be wondering, "if personal resolve to overcome binge eating isn't enough, where do I begin?"

I found it helpful to examine my relationship with food so I could approach each meal or snack with enthusiasm rather than anxiety. Like my dad, I developed an unhealthy relationship with food. I ate when I was bored, frustrated, or if the clock indicated it was "time to eat". I ate in times of celebration—at parties, after the high school football team won a game, and when I aced a test. I ate when meeting with friends and family. I also turned to food in times of emotional crisis—a breakup with a boyfriend, a lower than expected grade, nervousness before a choir or band concert, etc. Over the years, food developed into what felt like an effective and acceptable coping mechanism, a security blanket. Whenever I felt upset, I knew eating would calm me down. Most often I'd eat more than just "a snack"; I'd binge. Bingeing slowed me down physically and mentally and allowed me to forget about the real issues troubling me. However, a whole new set of problems arose with each binge: "How many calories did I just eat?" "I'll definitely gain weight from that." "Tomorrow I'll have to be extra strict with what I eat." Yet, as much as these new concerns burdened me, I felt I could handle them. After all, I had "solutions" to these issues. I didn't have quick answers to the more complex stressors like "How will I survive without a boyfriend?" or "I'm a failure because I got a lower grade than I expected."

Bingeing became my crutch during high school. Like many teenagers, I came home each afternoon "stressed out"—nervous about upcoming tests, manic about getting my homework done before dinner and my flute music practiced, and worrying about what everyone at school thought of me. I dealt with that stress by jumping in B.E.D. Although I generally ate anything in the house, two of my favorite binge foods were brown sugar and chocolate chips. Brown sugar was instantly satisfying. I enjoyed the rich flavor of it and the way a grainy, hardened lump of it melted on my tongue. Semi-sweet chocolate chips were even more grand; they could be popped in my mouth one at a time over and over again until gone or they could be tossed in by the handful, resulting in a mini explosion of chocolaty goodness. Both foods could be quickly shoveled into my mouth if the need to get rid of "the evidence" suddenly arose. (At least, they were more easily shoved in there than say, a cupcake, which I would have preferred to eat.)

An added plus to bingeing on chocolate chips and brown sugar was that they both came in bulk bags; I knew my mom wouldn't notice that a few more tablespoons were missing each week. I was so afraid of the shame of being caught eating foods that weren't really meant for consumption in their "raw" state. I also knew my mom was aware of my dad's binge eating habits and worried that she would suspect I was going through something similar. I didn't want to let her down; I had thought of myself as her "good girl" and desperately wanted to maintain that image. I worried that her finding out about my binges would mean a crackdown on the kinds of snack foods she brought into the house or, even worse, a confrontation about my eating habits. So, I did whatever I could to hide my habits. Once, after I polished off a bag of semi-sweet morsels, I walked down to the corner store and bought a new bag, ate a third of them, and put the rest back in the tin they came from, feeling sure that she'd never know.

While it was always important that I binged in secret, w*here* I binged was less important to me. If it was private and provided me access to a lot of food, I'd make it work. Most days, I binged at home, standing behind the open pantry door, as I had often seen my dad do. Occasionally I took piles of food to my room and locked the door behind me. Once I took a handful of pretzels and a bag of cookies outside, climbed the big maple on the corner of our property and ate everything while nestled among the tree branches, my eyes glued to the back door, ready to stash the food further up the tree in case anyone approached me.

One summer I had a less-than-desirable job at a local ice cream shop. The hours were long, the work (for a previously un-worked 16-year-old) was hard, and the pay was meager. However, I was told on my first day that I could have up to two scoops of free ice cream per shift. It was a perk I couldn't pass up, and the discount I earned on half gallons of ice cream was exciting to my dad, as well. For most of the summer, I stuck to my two scoops a day, mindful that I shouldn't make it a habit to binge at my place of employment. A few times, however, I binged during my breaks, shoveling peanut butter and fudge-covered vanilla ice cream into my mouth in giant spoonfuls while huddled next to the extra tubs of vanilla ice milk in the walk-in freezer. Other times I'd volunteer to go to the storage room to refill the sundae toppings, knowing I could get away with eating a few handfuls of sprinkles, chocolate chips, or maraschino cherries before heading back in to the store.

I worked and binged at the ice cream shop off and on for a year, continually challenging myself to "Get a grip! Stop eating ice cream!" When I got to college the following year, I worried I'd gain the infamous "freshman fifteen". I vowed to exercise more, eat less, and avoid certain "bad" foods. I did pretty well for the first few weeks, mainly because I was so busy meeting new people, figuring out the campus, and establishing a new routine.

However, about a month into freshman year, I discovered a spot on campus where the food was free and the risk of getting caught was relatively low. My bingeing became rampant.

Moving my B.E.D. to the chapel kitchen

My first year of college was both exciting and lonely. Having never been away from home for more than a week, I was quite homesick off and on for the first month. Fortunately, I had signed up to participate in the marching band, and band members got to arrive on campus about two weeks before anyone else. We did some indoor practicing of the music and spent a lot of time out on the practice field learning the drill in preparation for halftime at the first football game. Being there early was a really nice introduction to the school prior to the frenzy of activity that occurs on Freshman Move-In Day.

So, when that big day arrived, I was already acquainted with many people. One of those people was a member of the college's Chapel Choir and before I knew it, I was auditioning for that, as well. Being a member of the choir presented me with the opportunity to make a whole new group of friends and gave me an increased level of comfort. As a "P.K.", or "Pastor's Kid", church had always been like a second home to me. The college chapel was no different. In fact, it became all-too-similar to home once I discovered it had a kitchen.

I'm sure I knew the kitchen was there all along, but it wasn't until I felt completely at ease in the chapel that I started to obsess about it and wonder whether or not I could binge there. The kitchen was continually restocked with food; every week a new supply of donuts, cookies, and pretzels (leftover from the weekly fellowship hour) appeared. At first I would go in there for a legitimate snack. Feeling hungry, I'd think, "Well, I'm here. And the food is here. I'll just have a cookie or two." Certainly, other students helped themselves to small snacks from time to time, as well. But because the kitchen was tucked away from the main offices and because of my history of disordered eating, it felt wrong to be in there. I was ashamed to be eating what I considered "junk food" and to be eating between meals no less, so I didn't tell anyone when I ate something. Often, my guilt was so strong, I considered myself a criminal, as if I had *stolen* my food from the kitchen.

Despite this guilt, I felt powerless to avoid the kitchen whenever few people were around. If I made up my mind to go in the kitchen and eat, I had the same physiological feelings of nervousness that I experienced when trying to sneak something from the pantry closet at home without being seen. My cheeks flushed, my heart beat faster, my palms got sweaty and I was on heightened alert for the sound of footsteps. If necessary, I could flee to the small reading room next to the kitchen. In fact, a few days into this kind of behavior, my anxiety became so acute that I began to "stage my act" in order to cover myself; if I heard anyone coming I could dart into that reading room and grab my textbook (which I would have put in there earlier) and act as if I was just doing homework.

I felt the need to come up with an "escape plan" because the very thought of being seen eating between meals was terrifying. A bombardment of questions like "What if I get caught?" and "What if s/he thinks I'm fat?" and "What if s/he tells someone else?" plagued me every time I stepped into that kitchen. At home I felt a little more comfortable eating between meals; my dad did it, and even if I got caught I knew my parents wouldn't dislike me. But my first year at college, I believed that what I looked like and what people saw me eating would influence their opinions of me. Just like high school, I wanted to fit in. And just like high school, I turned to bingeing as a way of dealing with stress. I couldn't stop.

I got caught during a binge just once in the four years I was at college. I can still remember it clearly. It was a rainy October night during my sophomore year. I had just left the cafeteria and gone over to the chapel to do some studying. I glanced into the kitchen as I walked past. Five donuts were sitting in a box on the counter. Having just finished dinner I wasn't even remotely hungry, but within minutes of starting my work, I felt "called" to the kitchen as if each lovely little treat had two eyes, a mouth and a gaping hole where the nose should be. Just knowing they were in there, free and easily accessible, made eating them seem unavoidable. The fact that no one was around that night made them even more appealing. I left my books in the study room in their standard staged position and crept into the kitchen.

I intended to eat all five donuts, but just as I shoved the last bite of the first one in my mouth and reached for another, an acquaintance popped his head into the kitchen. My cheeks went red and I must have looked guilty because he said "Oh, sorry!" and ran out of the room as if he had just caught me with my shirt off. I hurriedly put back the second donut I was about to eat, grabbed my books and walked back to my dorm room. Self-loathing and shame were my constant companions, berating me the whole way back. I cursed myself for not hearing his footsteps, for being a "pig", even for making myself look guilty once caught. With my roommate absent and my stash of pretzels, cereal, and pop-tarts within easy reach, I finished my binge in the privacy of my dorm. As I crawled into bed that night (having been in B.E.D. for many hours), I vowed to never eat donuts again.

But, of course, that vow was soon broken. Just a week later, I was back in the kitchen with someone I had befriended freshman year. He was a charismatic, outspoken young man with whom I had felt an immediate connection. He made me laugh with his outrageously brash speeches. When we were together, I felt comfortable with my body because he was heavier than I was. I knew that I could never eat "too much" in front of him, so we frequently ate dinner together. After dinner, he or I would remark, "Let's go to the chapel to do our homework." We both knew that although we would eventually get around to doing our homework, we were really thinking, "Let's go to the chapel to see what leftovers are in the kitchen." We often binged together. Perhaps consuming large quantities of food was an attempt to fill the void our mutual hunger for straight A's had left within us. This particular night, after we had both polished off three donuts, the guilt began to sink in. I'll never forget the depth of my understanding when he said to me, "I should *not* be doing this, Megan. But I just can't help it."

I, too, felt helpless to prevent a binge. Each time I felt the urge to binge, I convinced myself I was powerless to stop it, totally out of control. I had been bingeing an average of three times a week for the five years leading up to my freshman year of college. The only way I knew how to avoid a binge was to completely rein myself in by keeping close tabs on every single thing that went in my mouth. That meant recording my daily weight, keeping track of my caloric intake at all times (on paper or in my head), and not eating any food that I thought would make me fat—cake, cookies, donuts, pie, pretzels, chips, bagels, muffins, brownies, ice cream— just about everything I loved to eat. If I didn't eat these things, I felt good about myself. I felt if I could control that part of me, I would be beautiful, successful, well-liked, and happy. But as I said earlier, eventually I would crack. I'd allow myself "just one bite" and one bite would turn into a mountain of food gobbled up in the span of just a few minutes.

Of course, after eating a lot, I felt bloated and stretched like an over-filled water balloon. If I had to go out in public after bingeing, I was convinced that I was noticeably fatter. I imagined myself as a gigantic round blueberry lumbering along like Violet from "Willy Wonka and the Chocolate Factory" after she eats the untested full-course meal bubblegum and has to be rolled away by the Oompa Loompas to be drained. Most often, though, after a binge I stayed in the privacy of my home, dorm room, or apartment, so I just changed into sweat pants or pajamas to avoid the feel of my jeans digging into my stomach. I often felt nauseous and wanted to throw up but never did, believing that forcing myself to throw up would be far more destructive in the long run than consuming large quantities of junk food. The curious thing about Binge-Eating Disorder is that despite such physical and emotional discomfort every time I binged, I felt helpless to prevent another one. I was stuck in the terrible grip of a monster, but I didn't yet understand that I had a real disorder. After all, these were things my own father had done as long as I could remember and, as far as I knew, there was nothing wrong with him. I continued to binge regularly throughout my college career, ever hopeful that my bingeing would stop after graduation. I was engaged to be married, moving into my own place and beginning graduate school to pursue a degree in counseling. I would finally have the chance to really take control of my eating. No more chapel kitchen to raid. No more cafeteria all-you-can-eat meals. Yes, things were going to be different from now on.

Binge More in Baltimore

In August of 1999, after graduation and one last summer working on campus, I left college and moved to a small town just outside of Baltimore, Maryland. I was preparing to enter my first semester as a graduate student in a Counseling Psychology program. I moved into a rented, off-campus townhouse and soon found a part-time job as an activities assistant at a local nursing home. While I certainly made friends at school and work, I hesitated to really "grow roots" because I knew I would only be there for two years. I thus remained somewhat emotionally distant from those I met, longing mostly for the company of my British fiancé, who had two more years of college in England before he'd be moving to the States.

Many nights, alone in my spacious two-story townhouse with my homework done (at least a day before it was due) and dinner eaten, I found myself bored and lonely. Unable to afford cable TV, I had about six channels to watch. (There are only so many reruns of *Seinfeld* I could watch without feeling like I wanted to rip my hair out.) With nothing to capture my attention and little desire to go out by myself, the conditions were ripe for bingeing. I would pace back and forth between the living room and the kitchen in search of something which would satisfy me. Hoping to keep myself in check in my new environment, I rarely bought junk food, so there wasn't much of anything to binge on. In fact, I was so afraid of spiraling out of control that I continued to keep strict tabs on my food intake, often preparing for myself a pathetically lean dinner of boiled rice and steamed broccoli. After a bland meal like that, it's no wonder I wanted to binge on cake, cookies, donuts, and ice cream. If the urge to binge came on late at night and I didn't feel like going out to buy food, I ate bowl after bowl of cereal. When that was gone, I turned to raw granulated sugar. (That particular habit started in college one night after I ran out of pre-sweetened Kool-Aid granules, which I had been eating like Pixi-Stix straight out of the container with a plastic spoon.)

Once in a while, the urge to binge was really strong. If I had enough money to spare (which wasn't always the case since I was only working part time and was paying my way through grad school), I'd hop in my car and drive to the 24-hour donut shop for a dozen glazed delights hot out of the fryer. I'd get flushed and sweaty when paying for them, nervous that others could see right into my brain and know that I was going to eat them all myself. I was ready with a prepared speech if anyone asked: "Oh, it's my turn to bring a treat to my book club tonight." I wasn't even in a book club. Without really being aware of it, I was again grabbing those familiar security blankets, using food to fill a void, just as I had done throughout my adolescence and college. Sometimes that emptiness was emotional—brought on by loneliness, the pressures of grad school, or feelings of worthlessness. Other times it was simply having too much unstructured time on my hands or even just easy access to food.

My part-time job as an activities assistant at a local nursing home provided me with both free time and accessible food. I worked three days a week plus every other Saturday. Since our activities department was limited to two full-time and three part-time staff members, the weekend shifts were usually conducted solo. During my shift, I would be responsible for helping the residents to and from the dining room at lunch and organizing the early afternoon movie. Once the movie was started, my time was to be spent visiting with the room-bound residents and carrying on another activity on the second floor.

I have always tried to be an efficient worker, believing in the "work before play" philosophy such that "the sooner 'x' is done, the sooner I can relax." (I have since realized that the work is *never* done and that if I lived my life by the "work before play" rule, I'd probably die of a stress-induced heart attack by age fifty.) My duties on Saturdays were usually finished an hour before my shift was over. Instead of providing the residents with extra visits, organizing a reading group, or making some other productive use of my time, I chose to wait behind the closed door of the activities department until it was time to leave. It just so happened that the room was continually stocked with food for the various events we hosted for the residents—everything from hard candy and chocolate bars to snack-sized packs of crackers and balls of frozen cookie dough which we baked and sold for fundraisers.

During the last hour of my Saturday shifts, I binged on as many of those things as I could. Like a twisted homage to my frozen cake eating days in high school, I even ate frozen cookie dough; I especially liked the cloying sweetness and grainy texture of the oatmeal raisin kind. But I agonized over each thing that went into my mouth, weighing up the risk of being caught, the knowledge that over time I could gain weight if I kept eating that much, and the fact that if I ate too much, someone would surely notice the missing food. In addition, I was weighed down with guilt from eating the residents' snacks. I imagined their looks of disappointment when there were no packs of Oreos or Lorna

Doones to be won as prizes at the next bingo game. To make myself, and potentially them, feel better I took note of those foods which were less desired by the residents and forced myself to binge only on those things: after dinner mints, snack bags of potato chips, and peanut butter crackers. I spent hours hating myself after each binge. Yet every Saturday it was the same thing. The extra time and total privacy of the office, coupled with my boredom, loneliness, and love of sweets provided plenty of sway to perpetuate my bingeing.

Shortly before the end of my first year of grad school, some part of me decided I wasn't ready to be a counselor. I didn't feel confident in my ability to counsel others when I felt so in need of counseling myself. I hemmed and hawed about my decision, but ultimately dropped out of the program. I picked up some extra hours at the nursing home while I looked for a full-time job elsewhere. I was eventually offered a job in Philadelphia as a research assistant in the field of Neuropsychology. On my last day at the nursing home, I told one of my co-workers about my bingeing, relieved that no matter what she thought of me after I told her, at least I wouldn't have to continually see her looks of disappointment or pity. I explained the helplessness I felt to prevent a binge or stop one while it was occurring. I told her how guilty and ashamed I felt and talked about how I restricted calories for a while after a binge. (I never did tell her about all the food I stole from the activities department cabinets, though I suspect she and others must have known.) She listened intently. Much to my surprise she replied, "Honey, everybody does that!" Her belief that my eating was normal was all the justification I needed to continue with the same habits. Just as some have said, "You're just big boned" I told myself, "It could be worse." At the time, I didn't know just how much "worse" it could be.

Mirror, Mirror on the Wall [5]

After I moved to Philadelphia in July of 2000, my eating continued to spiral out of control. In addition to planning my wedding, I was dealing with the sense of failure for having

[5] Portions of this section are from my essay, "Smoke and Mirrors" published in *The Healing Muse: A Journal of Literary and Visual Arts*. Fall 2006. Vol. 6, No. 1, p. 30-31 (Reprinted by permission).

dropped out of grad school, and with the stresses of a new job, a new apartment, and new people to meet. At least four times a week, sometimes every day for weeks at a time, I gave in to the urge to binge. I felt incredibly guilty for eating so much, but just didn't know how else to deal with the pressures in my life. I continued to obsess over my physical shape and weighed myself at least once a week even though I agonized over "weigh day".

Someone who isn't stuck in B.E.D. or dealing with another eating disorder can probably get on the scale, look at the number and realize that it's just a number. I, however, looked at the number and *became* the number. My journal entries are full of statements saying, "Ugh. Today I was *148*." or "I'm feeling good because I'm only 143!" Long ago, I had lost the ability to see more than just the physical part of me and since I was rarely satisfied with that part, I constantly worked to change it. I remember feeling dismayed when, at my last wedding gown fitting in July 2001, the seamstress had to let out the seams a bit to accommodate my weight gain. This was the only time in my life when I was actually overweight for my height. At 168 pounds, I was even more disgusted with my body than ever before. I kept telling myself, "I have to lose at least ten pounds before the wedding" but every time I put myself on a strict diet, I went off of it within days, caving in to some tempting food, and then binged in order to numb the pain I felt from having failed yet another diet.

Two months after the wedding, my husband decided he wanted to lose some weight. He cut all snacks out of his diet and drastically reduced his portions at meals. He started weighing himself every day and wrote his average weight each week on a dry erase board we had hanging in our study. Seeing his numbers drop consistently, I felt increasingly nervous that he would soon be lighter than me. I remembered the security, albeit temporary, I had felt whenever I would hang out with my overweight college friend. I couldn't bear the thought of being fatter than my husband. In fact, I regularly served him larger portions at dinner than I allowed myself to eat, hoping to avoid that potential crisis. When I realized he was still dropping the pounds, I focused all my energy on my own weight loss instead of sabotaging his. I started recording my weight each day and writing the weekly average up on the board. It didn't take long for me to notice that, although the pounds were coming off, I wasn't losing weight as quickly as my husband was. I began to dread sharing "my number" with him. Since my weight was now bound to my self-worth, I agonized that his opinion of me was also dependent on that number. Of course, I wasn't thinking rationally (I never had been able to when it came to food, body image, or weight): perhaps he needed to lose more weight than I did. I reminded myself that weight-loss experts say that slow weight-loss is easier to maintain than a quick drop in pounds, but my anxieties continued.

As the days and weeks went by, I grew suspicious of the scale; sometimes the number seemed to accurately reflect how I felt (usually either "fat" or "okay"), and other times it seemed way off ("I can't possibly be *that* thin!"). I began to confirm how I felt with what I saw in the mirror, especially on days when the number on the scale was much higher or lower than I expected. It never occurred to me that my perception could be distorted. I just assumed the mirror wouldn't lie; whatever was reflected in it was the truth. (Indeed, I had been looking at myself in the mirror every day for years prior and "seeing was believing".) Consequently, I looked at myself all the time, trying to gauge whether I was, indeed, "fat" as the scale indicated or whether I was actually "skinny". I tried to tell myself, "It doesn't matter what number is on the scale as long as I look good." Of course, it wasn't long before the only things I looked at in my reflection were the ring of fat around my stomach, the flab on my thighs, my sagging upper arms, and my slight double chin. I was no longer able to even see all of the physical part of me. My entire self-image was based on just a fraction of the whole me.

What I saw in the mirror each morning, much like the number on the scale, directly influenced my eating patterns for that day. If I looked "good" or "skinny", I ate a little bit more than my usually strict diet plan allowed. Of course, then by the end of the day, the knowledge that I had eaten potentially fattening foods caused me to see nothing but a fat person in the mirror. If I thought I looked "fat" or "disgusting" in the morning, I ate even less than I would have otherwise, so of course by that evening, I'd look in the mirror and see a "good" person, a "skinny" person. As I continued to be a slave to the mirrors in my house, I also became conscious of reflective surfaces everywhere I went. When walking to my car, I would turn to the side to catch a glimpse of my profile once more before driving to work. When I arrived and closed my car door, I would again take a peek. Upon entering work, I would walk past the closed doors with glass windowpanes, stealing glances at myself in every one. Before leaving any private bathroom, I'd scrutinize my bare stomach from the front and both sides.

This devotion to my reflection (I would never call it "vanity" since I was rarely proud of my appearance), became routine along with the regular weighing, counting calories, restricting my intake, caving in to an urge to eat something I deemed "bad" and then crawling back into B.E.D. This continued until February of 2004 when I finally had enough of the binge cycle. In the three years since 2001 when I started trying to lose weight, I successfully shed close to twenty pounds (which I attribute to incorporating exercise into my daily routine) but I was still bingeing regularly. Despite the weight loss, I felt increasingly miserable about my physical shape and was soon desperate to make a permanent change in my eating habits. Ironically, that change was precipitated by a chocolate chip cookie; my wheel of fortune had spun full circle to the food that had seemingly started it all during my youth.

Chapter Four: Getting Out of B.E.D. for the First Time

from <u>In a Dark Time</u>

In a dark time, the eye begins to see…

--Theodore Roethke

One night in early February of 2004, I went to bed feeling lower than I'd ever felt before. Earlier that day I attended the monthly "birthday social" at work in which everyone in my department gathers in celebration for co-workers who have birthdays that month. There was a delicious spread of cakes, cookies, and brownies, along with the usual banter from some in the crowd: "Oh, I really shouldn't" and "Well, maybe just one" and "Thanks anyway. I'm on a diet." Despite my discomfort with my body, I kept my feelings to myself, recalling times past when any such verbalizations of my own were met with incredulous looks and comments like, "Why should you care? You're not fat!" or "Come on! You're young!" Not wanting to deal with this, I quietly enjoyed a slice of cake and a chocolate chip cookie and then went back to my office.

As the afternoon went on, I found myself increasingly unable to concentrate on my work. I couldn't stop myself from imagining that cake and that cookie sticking to my insides and making me fat. I felt miserable and chided myself for having given in to the temptation to eat fattening foods. I swore I would never eat such things again…starting *tomorrow*. After all, I had already "failed" by eating junk food, so why not enjoy what I could for the rest of the day?

Three times in the next few hours, I went back to the conference room where the leftover party foods remained out on the table for anyone to have. The first time I grabbed a brownie. On my way out the door, I noticed the secretary looking at me, so I smiled and said buoyantly, "I just *had* to try one of these yummy-looking brownies!" She smiled back and said, "Enjoy!" I finished the brownie before I even got back to my office, being sure to wipe my mouth with the back of my hand so my office mates wouldn't think I was a pig. About twenty minutes later, I walked back into the conference room a second time, under the guise of checking my mailbox. I knew that if the secretary was there, I was going to leave without any more food. I couldn't bear the thought of her seeing me go back for even *more*. But she wasn't at her desk. When I was sure no one else was around, I stacked two cookies on a plate, covered them with a napkin and practically ran down the hallway, holding my hand over the plate as if my body created an invisibility shield around my food. Back in the privacy of my office and feeling extremely anxious, I put the wrapped cookies in my empty lunchbox and decided to take them home for my husband. I resumed my work at the computer, all the while sensing my willpower slipping away like sand in an hourglass and acutely aware of the faint whimpering coming from within my closed lunchbox.

Ten minutes later, as the feelings of self-loathing consumed me, I reached for one of the cookies. I finished it in three quick bites as it continued to scream "EAT ME!" and then grabbed the other one, too. "Take that!", I thought, practically swallowing it whole. I told myself I would be "extra good" tomorrow and tried to continue typing. Within minutes I was chastising myself: "Not only are you fat and out of control, Megan, but you're a bad wife, too. Those cookies weren't for you." I decided to go back to the conference room one last time. Everything had been cleaned up and the secretary was gone for the day. But sitting on top of the microwave was the half-empty box of chocolate chip cookies. I glanced around the empty office suite and listened nervously for the approach of footsteps. Seeing and hearing nothing, I shoved two cookies in a napkin and headed out the door.

In the car on the way home, I told my husband I had a treat for him. He had kept off most of the weight he lost in 2001 by avoiding excessive sweets. However, he seemed quite pleased with my cookie offering that afternoon. For a little while, I was able to push aside my feelings of self-loathing and disgust, knowing that my gift was appreciated. But as the night went on, I grew more irritable and withdrew into myself. I didn't want to make or eat dinner. I didn't want to talk to my husband. Feeling full and lethargic, I couldn't concentrate on the movie we were watching. I hated myself for having eaten so much. I just wanted to go to bed so I could "start with a clean slate" in the morning.

I suddenly felt the gravity of the cycle in which I was caught. I realized I had been having days like this a few times a week for many years. At 5'9" and 150 pounds I was no longer overweight and yet the fear of gaining weight consumed me. I hated the way I had looked when I weighed 168 pounds and *never* wanted to weigh that much again. For years, I had been weighing myself and writing the numbers down religiously. Finally that night I thought, "This is enough! I have to tell someone about this."

So I did. I told my husband about the food I ate at the birthday party, my feelings afterward, my subsequent binge, and my self-loathing. I also told him it wasn't the first time I had done something like this. I talked about my obsession with my weight and shape, my history of bingeing in secret since I was a teenager, the severity of my binges back in Baltimore, and my recent realization that I needed real help. Telling him lessened the burden of guilt from my secretive binges, but it didn't solve the problem. I wanted to stop bingeing, to stop thinking about food all the time. Too ashamed and nervous to talk to a professional, I decided to take my treatment into my own hands.

The next morning marked my first attempt to get out of B.E.D. and shed the security blanket with which I had grown so comfortable. I began by tackling what I thought was the biggest problem: the bingeing itself. I didn't realize that my binges were the result of distorted thinking. I just figured if I didn't eat junk food I wouldn't feel nervous about gaining weight. If I wasn't gaining weight, I'd feel good about myself. If I felt good about myself, I wouldn't binge. It all seemed simple enough. So for the next three weeks, I lived on only fruit, vegetables, yogurt and minimal sugars and carbohydrates. Sometime in the third week of this self-imposed diet, I started having bouts of dizziness. After a few days of this, I began to get concerned. I decided to allow myself to eat a tuna hoagie for lunch at work one day, rather than just my usual fruit salad. After I had eaten about half of my hoagie I started to feel light-headed. I brushed it off as just anxiety about my upcoming team meeting that afternoon. But soon my arms and legs felt tingly and I felt myself getting hot. I stood up to alert my co-worker that I wasn't feeling well and within seconds of saying her name, I collapsed onto the floor of my office. She was able to revive me and get help, but in the process of standing up to get into a wheelchair, I fainted twice more and spent the night in the hospital with an I.V. in my arm. My diagnosis wasn't all that serious: "low blood pressure and low glucose (or "blood sugar") levels". Although the doctors asked about my current diet, I didn't tell them about my recent restrictions. I had a sinking feeling that getting out of B.E.D. wasn't going to be as easy as I thought.

As I lay in my hospital bed that night, I called a friend and told him about my binge eating and my attempt at a "cure all" which had landed me in the hospital. He was very concerned and asked if I was Anorexic or Bulimic. I paused. I had learned in one of my grad school classes that the symptoms I exhibited weren't 100% characteristic of either of those disorders. I was at a loss for what to call it. I binged like those with Bulimia, but I did not take laxatives or make myself throw up afterwards. I restricted my food intake like someone with Anorexia, especially the day after a binge, but never to the point of physical discomfort or starvation. But, characteristic of both anorexia and bulimia, I had intrusive thoughts about my body, my weight, and food on a daily basis. These thoughts often consumed me and prevented me from really enjoying my life.

Although I didn't know whether I had a diagnosable eating disorder or not, I knew I had a serious "problem with food". However, in order to regain my strength and my health, I would have to do as my doctors advised: increase the carbohydrates and sugar in my diet and eat smaller, but more frequent meals. This plan scared me. I worried that eating more often might cause me to go overboard and slip back into bingeing or worse yet, that I would gain weight.

However, I was able to stay on target with this new way of eating for nearly three months. I wasn't any less concerned about food, but at least I wasn't bingeing. Then, at the end of an emotionally shattering week in May, I couldn't take it anymore. I crawled back into my B.E.D. for escape and comfort. I binged three nights in a row. Each time, I waited anxiously until my husband wasn't looking and then felt a wave of relief wash over me followed shortly thereafter by a trance-like state during which time I headed to my usual binge spot in the kitchen and ate some of everything I could get my hands on: pretzels, chips, strawberry jam, cookies, milk, bread with butter, chocolate chips, hastily made butter icing, and granulated sugar. During the binges I felt numb and that numbness felt good. Soon after each binge, however, my self-loathing returned. I felt as though I had failed myself again, but I didn't want to stop bingeing. The memory of those few moments without emotional pain, without nagging thoughts, was enough to draw me back into B.E.D. time and again. My husband and I were in the beginning stages of a difficult separation and eventual divorce. Bingeing was the easiest and quickest way to deaden the pain. The problem was that it was part of a vicious, persistent cycle, one that I had vowed to free myself from months ago.

Being caught in the never-ending binge cycle was akin to hitting the snooze button on my alarm clock every ten minutes for fifteen years. By the time I really opened my eyes, sat up, and looked in the mirror, I was Rip Van Winkle waking up from an unbelievably long, but draining slumber. I hardly recognized my reflection. I had lost so much of who I once was and I wasn't becoming the woman I had aspired to be. I no longer sang, wrote poetry, read classic literature, or went out with my friends. I was cynical about true love and jealous of any woman who looked good, seemed confident, or was achieving her dreams. When my mom recommitted herself to musical pursuits like she had always longed to do, I grew angry and resentful. Instead of embracing or even learning from her, I withdrew from her altogether. In my attempt to attain an elusive physical shape, I had sacrificed the sources of happiness and release which were once an integral part of me. The weathered 27-year-old in the mirror was not at all appealing.

Having experienced even those brief months away from my B.E.D., I again wanted to feel that happy, or even happier. I found the strength within me to emerge from beneath the covers of my B.E.D. and told my parents about my years of bingeing and obsessive thoughts about my body and my weight. To my surprise, my dad admitted to having similarly disordered eating habits. My mom did some research and discovered not only a name for my symptoms (Binge-Eating Disorder) but a self-help book about how to overcome them.[6] As I read through the first few chapters of Dr. Christopher G. Fairburn's book, *Overcoming Binge Eating*, I saw myself on every page. I began the suggested activities with enthusiasm, anxious to see some progress towards recovery.

During my counseling session the following week, I told my therapist, Pat, about my eating disorder and new hope for

---

[6] Fairburn, Dr. Christopher G. (1995). *Overcoming Binge Eating*. New York: Guilford Press.

recovery. It was difficult to admit to myself that I needed help for yet another major issue in my life; my weekly sessions, in which I was still working through the residual pain of my failed marriage, were emotionally draining. I couldn't imagine what I'd have to go through to come out on the other side of yet another dark forest. But an old phrase came to mind, challenging me from my despair: "The first step to recovery is admitting you have a problem." So I took it upon myself to tell as many people as I could that I have Binge-Eating Disorder. I had already told my parents, my therapist, and my boyfriend, Isaac, about my past and present struggles, so I began telling friends with whom I had long ago lost touch. Reconnecting with those I had neglected was therapeutic in itself, but I still felt it was important to tell them of my trials. The more words of encouragement I received, the more buoyed up I felt. My head was finally above water again. But I worried about how I'd keep it up.

My therapist suggested that simple awareness of what triggered my binges might give me the power to at least break a link in the binge cycle. At that point, I was willing to try anything. I knew if I could get out of B.E.D. long enough to experience the joy of living my life to the fullest, getting (and even staying) out of B.E.D. on other days would be that much easier.

Becoming aware of my binge triggers required daily journaling and a commitment to reviewing those entries periodically. While searching my words for the common threads that had woven together my once comfortable B.E.D. covers, I was forced to find within me a gentler self, one who could encourage me throughout my recovery. It was that kind voice within me that persuaded me to write the following journal entry in the midst of my despair:

> I'm so full right now I feel as though I could burst. I ate way more tuna casserole for dinner tonight than I should have. And then when I got home to the empty apartment, I just shoveled chocolate into my mouth until I thought I'd throw up. Why do I keep bingeing?! I'm so disappointed in myself. I feel like I'm nearly back to square one as far as the frequency of my binges.
>
> These days I've been obsessing more and more over the shape of my body and how much exercise I've done or not done. I've been comparing myself to everyone—strangers, friends, co-workers—worrying about every inch of fat on my body. I've felt less interested in sex and ashamed of myself for not being in better control of everything. Two weeks ago, I had three binges in the span of six days. Now I just finished my 4th binge in 5 days!
>
> I wonder where I've gone wrong…I was doing so well for a few months. How did I lose control again? It seems to start with just one day of feeling like I ate something I 'shouldn't have' and then it spirals into this hopeless attitude of 'oh, well. I screwed up *again.*' Whenever I think I've regained control over my eating, and give myself permission to eat something really tasty, my negative brain takes over and says, 'Well, that's it. You might as well eat everything you want, since you ate that last treat. Just write off today as a failure and start over again tomorrow.'
>
> --Excerpt from my journal, 3/24/05

My first few attempts to get out of B.E.D. were quite difficult. Going for more than a day without bingeing seemed impossible. Whenever I closed my eyes, I saw what looked like a factory's "accident-free" sign, only mine read, "_2_ Days Binge-Free". If I made it through two days, I felt like celebrating and did so with foods I had been avoiding. Shortly thereafter, though, the guilt crept in like an intruder in the night. Since I was familiar with this particular intruder, he seemed more like an unwanted houseguest than a threat. He was quite persistent, constantly nagging me for slipping up. It didn't take long before I was totally swept up in the binge cycle again. If I closed my eyes I could see that the new sign said: "_0_ Days Binge-Free". The constant feeling of having to start over was so discouraging. It never occurred to me that I was looking at my progress all wrong.

As I continued to talk with my counselor and work through Dr. Fairburn's six step self-help program[7], I learned that I would have to identify ways to free myself from the binge cycle. In order to gain deeper insight into what triggered my binges, I kept a food journal and tried to establish a pattern of regular eating. That meant keeping track of everything I ate each day and forcing myself to eat at least four times a day so I wouldn't have that "starved" feeling which I already knew was a sure trigger for a rapid intake of food. I decided to eat every four hours: breakfast at 8am, lunch at noon, a snack at 4pm, and dinner at 8pm. It was comforting to me that the first step in my recovery involved establishing an eating routine. After all, I had always wanted to have strict control over what I ate and when.

In addition to these techniques, my counselor recommended I keep a daily "balance inventory", a log of my mental, emotional, physical, and spiritual well-being. The goal was to nurture all four areas of my life each day. I could provide myself with mental stimulation (e.g. – attending a lecture at work or reading an interesting article), emotional growth (e.g. – reaching out to a friend I hadn't talked to in a while), physical health (e.g. – exercising), and spiritual growth (e.g. – re-connecting with my spiritual side). Rarely one to shy away from an assignment, I tackled both the food journal and the balance inventory with vigor,

---

[7] Fairburn, Dr. Christopher G. (1995). *Overcoming Binge Eating*. New York: Guilford Press. p. 140 (Reprinted by permission).

attending to them daily. Neither was particularly difficult to write, but admitting when I had binged was. I didn't particularly like to admit when I had crawled back in B.E.D. I imagined someone finding my journal in a pile of books at a yard sale someday and poring through it one night with a feeling of utter disgust that the author wasn't able to just get a hold of herself and stop bingeing. Of course, that was ridiculous and I knew that in order to discover what led to my binges, I'd have to be honest with myself and write down every one. As time went on, that got easier. Below is an entry from my journal. I've highlighted a few of the stressors that continually triggered a binge.

12/6/04 – I felt really bored at work today, despite having a lot to do. Some days it's just not challenging enough. I came home to the empty apartment and got a little manic while cleaning things up before mom and dad came over to see the place for the first time. When they arrived, I was nervous, but not overly so. They seemed to like it. After they left, I cooked dinner for me and Isaac. When he went back to work I felt uninspired and "blah." Not depressed, just not my chipper self. I was already feeling "bad" for having had two graham crackers and some cappuccino before dinner. I ate all my food at dinner and felt like I should have left some there.

Isaac's having an extra long night at work tonight. That means I'm gonna be home alone for a really long time. I ran out to Target and bought a bunch of Christmas decorations to put up. It took me over three hours to get the living room decorated and the whole time, I was scurrying around like a squirrel. I had this moment where I thought, 'I shouldn't have eaten so much today'. Soon after that, I went into the kitchen where I ate some M&Ms, a spoonful of peanut butter and a bite-size Butterfinger bar. Then I went back to work, but felt guilty for having eaten that stuff. Shortly thereafter, I found myself back in the kitchen eating more of the same things plus pretzels, cheese crackers, and cereal.

I think if I wasn't trying so hard to distract myself from eating, I would have realized sooner that I was feeling vulnerable tonight. Then I might have realized it was a good time for me to sit down and do some journaling...before the binge happened. But it's too late now. I knew the best thing to do was to at least write down what happened today so I could look back later and understand why I binged.

In the process of regularly keeping track of my food intake, my emotional states, my binges, and my overall well-being, it became clear that many different things seemed to trigger my binges: personal stress related to my family and my relationships, work-related stress, boredom, loneliness, hunger, fatigue, eating out, failure to live up to my own diet plans, etc. There seemed to be too many reasons to count and I wondered how I'd ever prevent any of those stressors, let alone *all* of them. As I looked more closely, however, it appeared that most of my binge triggers were negative emotions. It seemed that any time I experienced internal tension of any kind, I turned to food and bingeing. I thought back on all the times in high school, college, and grad school when I jumped in B.E.D. at the first sign of stress. Becoming aware of this link between my emotional state and my urges to binge was crucial. All I had to do now was either reduce the tension in my life or find alternative ways of coping with my negative emotions. Neither of those sounded like an easy task! But it felt good to have at least recognized some of the factors contributing to my disordered eating. Now I could stop thinking of progress simply in terms of "___ Days Binge-Free"; I was making progress simply by becoming aware of what triggered a binge.

Still, I worried about what to do if and when the urge to binge arose. I turned to Dr. Fairburn's self-help program for guidance: "to help you avoid eating between your planned meals and snacks, you will find it useful to have a range of alternative activities."[8] Since I now knew something about the triggers to my binges, I knew that the best way for me to avoid a binge would be to first and foremost "remove myself from the kitchen". However, just doing that wouldn't be enough; in my apartment, the living room was right next to the kitchen and sitting in front of the TV was another place I often felt the urge to binge. I'd have to not only stay away from the kitchen, but vacate the living room also. That left just two rooms of my little apartment in which to escape: the study or the bedroom. Thus, any alternative activities I wrote

---

[8] Fairburn, Dr. Christopher G. (1995). *Overcoming Binge Eating*. New York: Guilford Press. p. 171 (Reprinted by permission).

down would have to be able to occur in those rooms or outside the house altogether. After considering many different activities my top five included, "call a friend", "go for a walk", "read a book in the bedroom", "write a letter to someone", and "clean the bathroom".

Over the next few months, I employed my alternative activities whenever the urge to binge arose. Sometimes I was successful in avoiding a binge. Other times I was not. I remember feeling totally bored one evening and the urge to binge was crushing me. The Valentine's Day gift of *Godiva's* chocolates seemed to be announcing its presence to me every thirty seconds: "Eat us!"... "Eat us!"... "Eat us!" No sooner had I pushed away the thought, the image of thirty lovely-looking, mouth-watering, spherical treats popped unavoidably back into my head. I felt myself on the brink of madness, much like that *Simpsons* episode when Homer imagines himself on a journey through the Land of Chocolate, gleefully frolicking and skipping between giant chocolate flowers and chomping on a chocolate lamppost. The only difference was that my own breakdown would include a real life journey through "Godivaville" and wouldn't be nearly as carefree as his.

After enduring a few more rounds of "Eat us!"... "Eat us!", I decided to leave the house and go for a long walk. It felt great to be outside, away from the kitchen and those screaming chocolates. I began congratulating myself for avoiding a binge and was soon lost in thought about how difficult it was to stay out of B.E.D. When I had walked about half a mile, I suddenly realized where my feet were taking me: directly to the convenience store. "No! Don't go in there!" something inside me yelled urgently. I paused on the sidewalk for a fraction of a second. Without missing a beat, a more insistent voice reasoned, "Listen. You can't just turn around and walk home without buying anything. That would be pointless. And someone might think you're weird if you just walk up to the door, turn around and walk away." "You're right," I replied as I opened the door and absent-mindedly retraced the steps I had walked countless times before to the donut cabinet then the candy rack. Minutes later, I emerged and looked down in bewilderment at the glazed donut in my left hand and the Snickers bar in my right which was already unwrapped and half eaten. Feeling a glutton for punishment, I finished the Snickers and the donut before berating myself: "You're such an idiot. You were trying to *avoid* a binge. Not go out and spend money on one!" I was disgusted. I even considered crossing "go for a walk" off my list of binge-avoiding activities. I could have continued in this way for some time, but as I reached my front door, I remembered my counselor's advice: "Go easy on yourself, Megan." I tried to see the positive side of the situation: "At least it wasn't a full-sized binge." I reminded myself that a donut and a candy bar was only a fraction of what I used to consume during a regular binge. Even if I wasn't able to stop bingeing 100%, the frequency of my binges dropped from four or five times a week to just once or twice a week. As simple an idea it was to have a list of alternative activities waiting for me, it was an effective tool that made getting out of B.E.D. a lot easier.

Just as I kept up with my attempts to avoid bingeing, I also kept writing in my food journal and maintaining my balance inventory. Once a week I reviewed my entries, looking for patterns and thinking about ways I could break out of the binge cycle once and for all. By early 2005, I had made another discovery about my disordered eating. Negative emotions weren't the only things making me want to crawl back in B.E.D.; negative *thoughts*, as well, had been plaguing me for over a decade and seemed to be at the root of my self-loathing and obsession with weight and body image.

Chapter Six: Pillow Talk

from <u>Lost in Translation</u>

...all is translation
And every bit of us is lost in it.

--James Merrill

Most of us are familiar with the little voice inside us which talks to us when we're scared of something. Whether it's fear of failure (or even success), fear of what others think of us, or fear of losing control of ourselves, the inner critic knows us intimately. But instead of engaging us in sweet "pillow talk", he[9] continually tries to hurt us, often chiming in at the worst possible moment. When I reviewed my journal entries more closely, I saw that my critic was working overtime, constantly whispering not-so-sweet nothings into my ear: "You're so fat. You'll never amount to anything if you can't even control what you eat." or "Go ahead. Just eat whatever you want since you're already a failure." These self-critical thoughts were automatic and a regular part of my life in B.E.D. In fact, I'd had them so long, they seemed normal to me. When I reviewed the "emotional" component of my balance inventory, I discovered many of those automatic thoughts hidden between the lines of written text. To make this point clear, I've written them in parentheses in the following entries:

3/14/05—woke up feeling good about the way I look, (*"You were good yesterday."*) thus I didn't worry about eating some ice cream as a treat tonight (*"You deserve it!"*).

3/15/05—woke up feeling a little worried about the ice-cream that I ate last night (*"You should NOT have eaten that. Now you'll surely get fat."*), even though it was only one portion. I felt tempted by chocolate chip cookies and M&Ms at work, but I didn't give in. (*"Good job!"*) When I got home, I was restless and ate a few things while I was cooking. It wasn't a lot, but the variety of it freaked me

---

[9] I refer to my inner critic as "he" because it helps me distance my real self as much as possible from that other voice. What gender is your inner critic?

out a bit (*"You messed up your 'clean slate' for the day."*). I have to stay out of the kitchen for the rest of the night or I know I'll lose what little control I have. (*"You'll **really** be a failure if that happens."*)

3/16/05—I had been nervously avoiding sweets all day until I was offered a blueberry Danish and ate half of it. The rest of the day I was ruminating over the fact that I had given in and eaten junk food (*"Way to go! You ruined your diet yet again. You're a complete failure."*). On my drive home from work, I thought about how I'm not nearly as skinny as my ex-husband's new girlfriend. I came home and changed into jeans so I could go for a walk (*"You'd better exercise 'cause you're downright FAT compared to that girl."*)—but by that time I was totally frantic that the more time that passed without exercising, the fatter I was getting. It was totally insane. I couldn't get my shoes on fast enough. And I couldn't stop the negative thoughts, no matter how hard I tried. I collapsed in tears before I left for my walk, sobbing about this dizzying cycle of highs and lows. When I finally calmed down, I went for a long walk. I didn't eat any snacks after dinner; finally feeling better about myself. (*"Good. You're in control again. Now maybe you won't stay fat."*)

3/17/05—today was better than yesterday, but I still woke up feeling nervous about my body (*"You really can't afford to eat the way you did yesterday."*); it seems like whenever I have a really difficult day or night, it takes a few days to get completely back on track. (*"You'll be back on track when you've avoided everything you want to eat for several days."*)

3/18/05—felt pretty good about my body although I was trying hard to get some exercise done since I knew I'd be eating quite a bit at my friend's house for dinner tonight (*"The exercise you do will help prevent you from gaining weight at dinner tonight."*); it actually wasn't all that much food (*"You weren't a total pig."*) but then I bought a muffin and a chocolate egg and ate both rather than save one for another day. (*"Okay, you **were** a total pig."*) I shouldn't have eaten both. (*"Not only are you a failure,* *but now you'll be a fat failure."*) I told myself on the way home that I would ration them. (*"A good person, one who's in control of things, would ration them."*) One treat tonight and one tomorrow, but suddenly I just wanted to eat them both to get it over with so I could start tomorrow with a clean slate. (*"Eating treats is bad. You shouldn't be bad two days in a row."*) I think tomorrow I'll go for a longer walk (*"These treats tonight are sure to make you fat."*).

3/19/05—woke up feeling anxious about having eaten too much yesterday. (*"You are definitely fatter today."*) I don't have time to exercise until later tonight, but I'd really like to go for a walk right now (*"If you don't exercise, you'll gain even more weight between now and then."*).

As you can see, there are an awful lot of automatic thoughts lurking behind those words. What's even more striking is just how ridiculous (and contradictory) these thoughts seem. I was lost in any attempt to translate them into something meaningful! Yet, I somehow believed each thought and let it dominate my life, determining my every action. If you've ever seen someone manipulate a marionette puppet, you know that every little jolt of the puppeteer's hand on the strings causes an arm, a leg, or the head to move in some way, whether the puppeteer intended it or not. I realized that I was now the puppet and my inner critic was the puppeteer. If he said, "You're fat", I exercised more, cut back on calories or avoided the foods I really wanted to eat. If he said, "Good job—you only ate 1200 calories today", I allowed myself to enjoy some of the food I wanted, only to then hear him say, "Now you've done it! You're definitely fat." Too often these negative thoughts fed my desire to binge; they made my B.E.D., with its well-worn covers, look great. It's easy to see how the combination of negative emotions and automatic thoughts was like a pair of ultra-strength chains, shackling me to my B.E.D. and locking me into the binge cycle.

Being a slave to disordered eating and regular bingeing was bad enough, but on top of that, my automatic thoughts prevented me from achieving any of my goals or dreams. Looking back at one of the more difficult times in my life, these harmful thoughts are now apparent where they were once invisible to me. In January of 2000, as I sat in my grad school Developmental Psychology class, I thought, "There's no way I can be a competent counselor. Who would want to be counseled by someone as young and emotionally messed up as me?" At the time, I pushed the thoughts aside. I even tried to fight back with positive ones: "No one expects me to be a good counselor right away. That's why I'm in school." However, as the winter days slowly crept by, I heard the negative thoughts louder and more often. By early February I had decided (or rather, reacted to my puppeteer's insistent tugs), "I really can't do this." The puppet master was becoming increasingly demanding. Not only was he controlling my eating habits, he was influencing my self-worth, as well. At the time, though, I agreed 100% with my automatic thoughts. I withdrew from the program at the end of that semester. Less than a month later, the guilt I felt for having "given up" intensified my negative thoughts. I labeled myself "a failure" and tried to move on with a new career and life in Philadelphia, again looking forward to having a "clean slate".

So, in early 2005, when I understood the amount of aggravation these ever-present automatic thoughts had been putting me through, I decided to do something about them. My counselor reminded me during one session that a great way to get rid of negative thoughts is to replace them with positive ones, kind of like re-programming an outdated system. Since I no longer wanted my old system to remain "online", I spent hours and hours trying to turn it off while simultaneously powering up a new system, one which would allow me to think better of myself and even to celebrate the small successes.

Whenever I had a negative thought (e.g. - "You're so fat." or "You'll never be a good writer."), I wrote it down on a piece of paper. (By the end of one day, I had written fifteen persistent, intrusive thoughts.) Then I spent some time countering each thought with a positive statement. For example, "You're so fat" became, "I'm not overweight. I eat a well-balanced diet and exercise regularly." "You'll never be a good writer" became "I am already a good writer. The more writing I do, the more confident I'll feel." As I wrote my list, I made a conscious effort to change the pronouns from "you" to "I". Speaking in terms of "I am..." seemed much more personal than "You are..." It felt like taking the control away from my inner critic (who seemed like an entirely separate—and malicious—entity at times), and re-claiming it for myself. I imagined myself reaching up with a giant pair of scissors and cutting the strings that once held my head, arms, and legs at their will. Now, if my critic said, "Megan, *you've* failed again", I came back with, "*I* did the best *I* could today."

I continued trying to think of positive statements to counter each of the negative ones. I was surprised by just how difficult this was! Over the years, my critic had possessed me, transforming me into an expert at berating myself. It hardly seemed possible; I always tried to offer encouragement and support to others, so how could I have lost the ability to encourage myself? Being kind to myself, or forgiving myself for not living up to my own expectations, seemed nearly impossible. Whenever I did come up with a positive statement that I truly believed, I forced myself to say it over and over again until it was memorized. Memorizing counter-thoughts was important because it allowed me to have a quick response whenever a negative thought popped into my head. I needed it to be as automatic as the negative one. The last thing I wanted to do was give that thought time to sink in while I scurried around the house looking for the paper on which I had written the counter-thought. It took quite a while, but by the fall of 2005, it seemed as though I had almost turned off my old system altogether. *Almost.*

One evening that fall, my boyfriend came home from a difficult night at work and needed to talk. I had had a stressful day myself and had decided to deal with it by crawling into B.E.D. rather than choosing one of my alternative activities. While bingeing earlier that night, I had been conscious of every bite of food I swallowed. It was an unusual state to be in; binges had previously provided me with at least a brief reprieve from stress during the numbness of a trance state. I knew there was a better way to deal with my emotional distress but the voice I heard that night said, "What's one binge when you've been so good for so long?" It made sense.

So I had just finished bingeing minutes before, when Isaac walked in the door. At the same time, the negative thoughts began infiltrating my consciousness, trickling slowly at first, like a thin stream of water flowing through a fissure in a dam, but soon bursting forth through a head-sized hole, washing over me and pushing me back with their sudden intensity and fury. I felt too tired to counter them with positive ones. "That's it! Now you've done it. You've ruined your whole day. Not just your day, but your whole month. You had been so *good*. What's your problem? You're such an idiot. You'll never be able to stop bingeing…" Could this really be the same voice that had just told me it was okay to binge because I had been so good for so long? I'm sure, as he told me about his rough night, Isaac had no idea I was being barraged with self-critical "pillow talk", but he probably did realize he didn't have my undivided attention. Before going to sleep that night, I wrote in my journal: "I tried to be a good listener, but felt distracted by my own self-hatred for giving in to a binge. The intrusive thoughts about my lack of self-control frustrated me because I wasn't able to give Isaac the support he deserved."

As I continued writing that entry, I forced myself to look at the positives: I was sitting here acknowledging my binge and my negative thoughts, and doing what I could to assess the situation so it didn't happen again. *That* was real progress. So *what* if I wasn't perfect? I was doing the best I could. I searched around the house until I found a crinkled slip of yellow paper on which my counselor had written a quote by Maya Angelou a few months earlier. I read the words several times, willing them to be the mortar that would patch up the hole in my dam, through which all those negative thoughts flowed forth:

> "You did what you knew how to do
> and when you knew better you did better."

I certainly did.

Chapter Seven: The "All or Nothing" Mindset

The quote by Maya Angelou inspired me often, yet just "knowing better" didn't always make it easy to "do better". I wondered if there was more to my automatic thoughts than I yet realized. Looking more closely at my food journal and my balance inventory, I discovered a pattern to my thoughts: they were most often dichotomous, or polar opposites, and they played me like a rope in the midst of a game of tug-of-war. For example, I described my days as either *good* or *bad*. I thought of myself as either a *success* or a *failure* depending on how much food I avoided or ate. I looked in a mirror or at the number on the scale and deemed myself *fat* or *thin*. Late at night, I allowed myself to eat *everything* in the kitchen or *nothing* at all. These opposing concepts, stark black or gleaming white, allowed for no possibility of gray. They pervaded many of my daily thoughts, whether they remained in my head or were written down on paper. It's hard to know how I developed such a black or white view of myself; it may have just been an easy way to lump myself into a category and proceed from there: "Since you were *bad* and binged and are now *fat*, you'll need to avoid *all* the foods you like." Of course, this didn't always work because those thoughts swept over me quickly, often changing in the span of minutes. For example, after having exercised for twenty minutes, I could walk past a mirror and think, "Bravo, Megan. You look good." A thought like that may have compelled me to reach for a snack to reward myself. But then just minutes later, with food in my mouth, I might notice my thighs and think, "Gross. You're so disgusting! Why are you eating?"

When it becomes difficult to see the gray areas of life, the in-betweens, or think in terms of a middle ground, one may be trapped in what some have called the "all or nothing" mindset. I realized I had lived much of my life thinking like that. I either ate *all* the food I wanted or I ate *nothing* I wanted. It wasn't until nine months after I first started getting out of B.E.D. and several months of reconnecting with family and friends from whom I had long ago isolated myself that I started to hear a more moderate voice. I had to listen hard through the static of the radio in my head in order to hear the faint murmur of "WLUV", in which the gentler voice was continually broadcasting this encouraging truth:

"You are beautiful as you are for who you are." Perhaps if I had been able to tune out WFAT or just known how to turn down the volume, getting out of B.E.D. might have been a lot easier. I might not have gotten caught in the binge cycle, believing that I would either be a fat, unlikable failure or a thin, adored success.

Throughout my adolescence and early adulthood, the all or nothing mindset played heavily into my automatic thoughts; every time I didn't live up to my self-imposed dietary rules (e.g. - "I'll only consume 1200 calories today") or stay within a certain narrow weight range (no more than two pounds above my average weight), I saw the word "failure" as if it was a gaudy red neon sign flashing its message to people near and far. I felt compelled to look at that sign and the more I stared at it, the deeper the word "failure" burned itself into my retinas and the longer it remained there after I closed my eyes to shut out its light. "FAILURE" led to a barrage of thoughts like, "I will *never* be *thin*. I will *always* be *fat*." and "Why bother to eat well if I'm doomed to be fat?" Feeling overwhelmed by what I saw as a miserable destiny, I often grabbed my security blanket and crawled into B.E.D. for a while.

It's not as though I felt altogether at ease with this solution. In fact, throughout my fifteen year stay in B.E.D., I made several attempts to turn off the electricity to that neon "FAILURE" sign. I figured if it couldn't light up, I wouldn't see it, and I wouldn't think of myself as a failure and better still, *others* wouldn't know I was a failure. So, I told myself, "Failure is not an option" and did the only thing I thought would prevent "FAILURE" from making an appearance: gradually I developed what became quite an extensive list of "forbidden foods", things which I liked to eat but which I deemed "too caloric" or had at one point triggered a binge.

You may recall from Amy's story that she, too, relegated certain foods to a "forbidden list". The fact that I even kept a list of "bad" foods is further evidence of my polarized thinking. Over many years, the list of foods I wouldn't touch grew longer and longer. The more I restricted from my diet and the longer I went without eating certain foods, the more difficult it was to resist those things if they were readily available to me. If I did allow myself to eat something from this list, I felt immediate intense guilt and disgust. The "FAILURE" sign lit up like the sun and I again fell into the first part of my binge cycle: obsession over my weight and shape. This caused me to design a strict diet plan for the next few days and eventually I'd be right back where I started: hiding under my B.E.D. covers, staring up at the flashing neon sign with sadness, anger, embarrassment, and frustration while its brilliance seared me to the core.

One of the many recommendations of the self-help program I had undertaken was to make a list of all my forbidden foods and slowly reincorporate them into my diet. The idea was to stop thinking in terms of "good foods" and "bad foods". The motto "everything in moderation" seemed to fit in there somehow. Moderation was a gray tone. It was never my forte, so this activity seemed like a great way to begin tackling my all or nothing mindset. I sat down to write my list one evening. I worked on it off and on for two days until I had what I thought was a complete list. There were over 75 foods staring me in the face:

Complete List of Forbidden or High-Anxiety Foods

cake	soft pretzels	cream cheese
cookies	milkshakes	cheesecake
pie	rootbeer floats	breaded chicken patties
tarts	pancakes	fast food
brownies	waffles	croutons
pastries	french toast	pizza
pop-tarts	cheesesteaks	breakfast sandwiches
crackers	meatball sandwiches	bagels
corn chips	macaroni salad	cream-based soups
sweet cereals	egg salad	mayonnaise
donuts	potato salad	white bread or rolls
non-diet soda	corn fritters	fried chicken
non-diet tea	nachos	bacon
ice cream	cotton candy	whipped cream
frozen yogurt	candy apples	nuts
water ice	funnel cake	chocolate milk
juices > 120 cal./serving	popcorn	milk > 1% fat
mangoes	potato chips	lattes
guava	french fries	mochas
pineapple	lasagna	cappuccinos
papaya	chocolate bars	frappuccinos
coconut	gummy candy	trail mix
avocado	marshmallows	rice pudding
guacamole	hot chocolate	chocolate pudding
hummus	fudge	mousse
veggie dips	sweet potatoes	dried fruit

It didn't seem possible I had been avoiding or fearful of so much all this time. But, in fact, the severity of my restrictions went back at least as far as October 1997, during my semester abroad at the University of Essex, in Colchester, England. I remember sitting at the table in my flat (one floor of a dormitory with private bedrooms and a shared living room and kitchen) eating a plate of steamed zucchini ("courgettes" as the Brits say) with Italian dressing. "What's that?" one of my flat mates asked while wrinkling his nose. "Zucchini", I replied and felt myself blushing as I thought, "Great. Now I'm gonna have to talk to him about why I'm eating so little." He read my mind. "Aren't you having anything else?" he asked. "No. I ate enough already today." I was hoping that would be the end of the subject. Instead he began to lecture me on the importance of eating "round meals". Since he was from Greece, I didn't bother to mention that they're called "square meals". I knew what he meant and that he was right, but I tried to make a joke of it instead: "I can't eat too many round meals or I'll become round myself!" I was just like my dad, unable to focus on anything but my physical self. To my surprise, my flat mate looked me right in the eye, a virtual stranger to me except for our shared living space, and said with a shrug, "You're pretty." I turned a deeper shade of scarlet as he left the kitchen and I was left alone with my unsavory pile of zucchini.

Despite the fact that he had thought (and told me) I was pretty, I refused to believe him. The critic inside me wouldn't allow any compliments to sink in. I wouldn't be pretty until the critic told me I was pretty and that wouldn't happen until I was thin and I wouldn't be thin unless I could control what I ate. The only way I knew how to control what I ate was by maintaining and living by that list of forbidden foods, as I had done for all those years. But now I was learning something different; the "forbidden list" *had* to go. But how?

I glanced at the list again and called to mind my recent daily diet: low-fat yogurt and 6 ounces of juice for breakfast, an apple and half a turkey sandwich (no mayo, no cheese) on wheat bread for lunch, pretzel sticks or a granola bar for snack, a meat and two veggies or a salad for dinner. It was pitiful. I had eaten virtually the same thing (or less) every day since I left grad school and moved to Philadelphia in 2000. Looking at this boring list of foods, it was no wonder I craved the cloying sweetness of processed carbohydrates like donuts, Tastykakes, and cookies. In fact, those were the first foods I turned to when bingeing. It was no wonder I felt nervous at the prospect of eating these things.

Following the self-help book's instructions, I ranked the foods from least to most anxiety-provoking: Potato chips, mayonnaise, white bread and sweet cereals were at the bottom of the list while donuts, ice cream, bagels and soft pretzels were nearly impossible to eat without feeling like a complete failure. I felt overwhelmed by the thought of trying to reincorporate seventy-some binge-triggering foods into my diet, but I knew I had to begin somewhere, so I started with the least anxiety-provoking items. The first day I made myself half a turkey sandwich...*with* mayonnaise. I never would have thought that mayo would taste so good. I stuck with that for a few days and then had a serving of potato chips one afternoon along with my half sandwich with mayo ("only a serving, cause I don't wanna go overboard", I thought). Eating two previously forbidden items in one meal made me nervous. I looked down at the white mayonnaise and small portion of chips and imagined them as millions of round fat molecules swimming down my gullet and getting immediately absorbed into my thighs and that small (but oh-so-noticeable to me) ring of fat around my waist. As soon as the molecules were nestled in to their new home, the neon "FAILURE" sign lit up for a few seconds. Starting to feel the effects of that message, I quickly destroyed the ridiculous image with a reminder that I was simply following the advice of an eating disorders expert. The sign flickered for a moment and then went out. The fat molecules popped like balloons and disintegrated as I told myself, "This is for my own good. If I want to make my daily decisions to get out of B.E.D. easier, I have to do this."

Close to a year later, I was regularly eating things that had at one point been on my forbidden list. However, I wasn't always successfully able to shut off the "FAILURE" sign, nor was I able to stop thinking dichotomously. I was still "good" or "bad", "thin" or "fat", "success" or "failure". Most often, I dwelt on the negative adjectives. In fact, in all those years, I was not once greeted with a beautiful bright "SUCCESS" sign in place of the "FAILURE" sign. Success was such a fleeting feeling that I barely even registered it. It was as if I so rarely thought well of myself that any positive statements were brushed aside: "Yeah, yeah. You didn't binge today. So what? You binged the previous three days, so don't get so excited about today." By allowing myself to only take notice of that glowing red FAILURE sign, I was unintentionally reinforcing that all or nothing mindset and chaining myself (even if on a long chain that afforded me some measure of freedom) to my B.E.D.

When I wrote the following I was still allowing dichotomous thoughts to dictate my behaviors:

> Isaac and I went for a long walk into Center City. On our way home we stopped at Wawa and, feeling good about having just exercised so much, I "treated myself" to a muffin and some cappuccino. The next morning I woke up, walked to the bathroom and looked in the mirror. "My cheeks are fatter. My chin is sagging. My stomach is softer. But how could that be? Well, I *did* eat that muffin yesterday. And I *have* been eating some chocolate every day. Well, I'll just have to stop. I wonder what I weigh this morning. Morning's really the best time to check. But, since I ate that muffin yesterday, I'd better not. Better wait 'til tomorrow or even Saturday so I have a few days to reset my system.

For two solid months after writing and reading that entry, I forced myself to find the gray areas of each situation. Rather than eating none of my forbidden foods or all of my forbidden foods, I could eat one of my previously forbidden foods and that was okay. I could be "doing the best I can" instead of just "a success" or "a failure." Each night when I filled out my balance inventory, I tried to characterize my thoughts appropriately, rather than push them to one or the other extreme. Believe it or not, by the end of those two months, I was able to write the following after a particularly difficult weekend in which I felt I had lost control over my eating:

> Part of me wants to just write off this weekend as a loss and call it quits. But I remember how great it feels to not binge. I know that I have the strength in me to not binge. I know I deserve to be kind to myself. I am taking the time to write this journal entry as a way of saying to my inner critic, "I'm stronger than you!" I must remind myself that despite feeling anxious about eating too much this weekend, I didn't binge today or at all this weekend for

60

that matter. I think I'll write a list of positive things I've done for myself and for others this week and then read and re-read the list until I feel strong again.

It still makes me smile when I read this journal entry. Despite feeling guilty about eating too much, I was able to see more than just the polar opposites. I was no longer controlled by a puppeteer or tugged back and forth like a rope between two arch rivals. I celebrated my small successes and didn't think of my temporary overeating as a failure. Finally, at this point in my recovery, I was able to look back at my B.E.D. with its well-worn covers and say, "You've served your purpose for long enough. I can handle this on my own now." I no longer needed the brief sense of security they had once provided. I had begun to understand and change my all or nothing mindset and was gradually seeing to it that I never again was trapped in the binge cycle.

Chapter Eight: My Toolbox

The Pen is Mightier than the Disorder

Breaking out of the binge cycle by dropping the all or nothing mindset was a critical part of my recovery. But my next move towards getting out of B.E.D. was to collect and then maintain a "toolbox" to which I could turn in case the urge to binge arose. When I first decided to get out of B.E.D., I thought that at some point my urge to binge would disappear completely. Unfortunately, that has yet to happen. At least once a week, I still feel that knee-jerk reaction and hear an automatic thought, "You'll feel better if you binge." Other times I see old photos of myself and think, "I must have gained ten pounds since then. What can I cut out of my diet so I can look like that again?" Fortunately, I've learned how to counter those thoughts with positive ones and am now able to rely on a few tried and true binge-fighting techniques to get me through the worst of it.

You may have heard the phrase, "the pen is mightier than the sword". It's an elegant way of reminding us that written or even spoken communication is a more effective problem-solver than a physical or violent reaction. In the early days of my recovery, I was surprised to discover that one of the most powerful tools available to me is my pen (or word processor), so I adapted the phrase for my own purposes: "the pen is mightier than the disorder."

I have always enjoyed writing (both journaling and creative writing), yet until my counselor suggested I keep a daily balance inventory and review it regularly, I never consciously thought my words could be therapeutic. Sure, I had scrawled countless poems and diary entries during difficult moments throughout my life, but I had never put the two together into an equation:

$$writing = therapy^{10}$$

When I began my balance inventory, I realized that getting my thoughts out of my head and onto paper (or the computer screen)

---

[10] I'm certainly not the first to note that writing—both journaling and creative—can be therapeutic; whole books have been written on the subject (see the "Resources" section for a short list).

was quite helpful. The act of linking my thoughts with my emotions was in itself rewarding, but reviewing my words later was even more beneficial. Take the following two early entries, one from a day when I felt well-balanced, calm and happy with myself, and the other from just a week later, on a day when my obsessive thoughts about food overwhelmed me:

10/24/04

Physical: went for two 25 minute walks; lifted weights for 10 minutes

Emotional: called mom to talk about my counseling session tonight; gave her some positive feedback about a decision she made; talked with her about how good it feels to be reconnecting with her

Mental: read a really interesting article in the *Council for Relationships* bi-annual newsletter (which dad gave me) called "Women and Rage" by Kimberly Flemke, PhD.; decided to write a journal entry about how I've experienced rage in my own life

Spiritual: had a spiritual moment when I was walking home on this crisp autumn evening; thought about how I've always felt strongly connected to the earth when she's in her state of "preparation" for winter; I love that sense of change/anticipation for the long, cold, dead months ahead, before the biggest most important rejuvenation of all.

*　　　*　　　*　　　*　　　*

10/30/04

Physical: went for a 20 minute walk

Emotional: it's so frustrating to me that I'll be okay about my weight & body image one day and then down about them the next. I just wish I had one solid day of not worrying about what I look like. When I looked at myself this morning, I saw nothing but a fat blob and saying, "I'm not fat. I eat a well-balanced diet and exercise regularly." wasn't helping. It annoys me so much to feel like this! I feel like just giving up and bingeing all night, kind of like "Well, if I'm already fat, why worry about it?" But I refuse to do that. I did eat a well-balanced diet and exercised today. I can't deny that those things are good for me.

<u>Mental</u>: read some of my book

<u>Spiritual</u>: none

*   *   *   *   *

It isn't hard to see that when I struggled with my body image and had to really work to resist the urge to binge, I had little or nothing to say about one or more areas of my life. As I reviewed more of my entries, this pattern appeared again and again. Although I already knew it first-hand, my writing revealed that the decision to get out of B.E.D., let alone act on it, was a daily battle. Some days, like the one above, it took so much energy that I had little left to devote to the other parts of my self. Yet, even then, it was (and still is) helpful to at least get the thoughts out of my head and onto a piece of paper. There they have a tangible form. If I want to exercise myself of my negative thoughts or preoccupations I can rip up the paper into tiny pieces and throw them in the trash. More often, though, I decide to keep my journal entries as a record. When I have a difficult day I can read what I've written and find comfort in the fact that there are patterns to my thoughts and behaviors. I can see the consistent triggers to my binges and be reminded of tools I have used to combat my disorder in the past. Most importantly, I am reminded that I have successfully avoided a binge on other occasions. For these reasons, I am never far away from a pen and paper; I carry them with me wherever I go.

While on vacation a few years ago, I frequently felt the urge to binge. I saw my friends and boyfriend eating whatever they wanted (seemingly without worry) and I thought "why can't *I* just kick back and eat whatever *I* want?!" Although I had successfully reincorporated some of my forbidden foods into my diet by that time, I was extra cautious while on vacation. I knew it would be easier for me to justify eating more than usual and that eating more than usual would possibly cause an increase in my weight. I wasn't confident that I could look at a higher number on the scale and remember that "I am not a number". There was a chance that I would feel "fat." Feeling fat could catapult me straight back into the binge cycle. I did not want that to happen. So I kept my pen at the ready during that vacation.

One night after my friends and I had finished a 10pm dinner, I was reminded of my self-imposed eating rule from previous years: "Don't eat after 9 o'clock or you'll get fat." (No doubt, I had made that rule after someone I admired as "a thin person" mentioned that she followed that rule.) "Way to go, Meg. It's *way* past 9 o'clock." With that one little thought, the floodgates opened. I couldn't stop obsessing about weight gain as a result of eating after nine o'clock. Instead of telling myself, "Yes, you ate after 9, but you got quite a bit of exercise today", my next thoughts were, "Crack open the ice cream! You won't look like you're overeating 'cause other people will eat it with you. Come on. Open it up! It's not like you were good today. In fact, you ate quite a lot today— breakfast, lunch, two snacks, *and* dinner! God, you're a whale! Just finish off the day with a tasty bowl of ice cream and then start over tomorrow with a clean slate. Tomorrow you can be *extra* good."

As soon as I realized I was about to jump head-first into B.E.D., I excused myself from the room, grabbed my pen and journal, and headed out onto the deck of our beach house. As I watched the last remnants of the sun sink below the horizon, I was reminded why I continued to get out of B.E.D. each day: to enjoy life. I looked out at the marshland behind our house and smiled at the pinks and oranges splashed across the sky. It was truly beautiful and serene. I wished I could absorb the peaceful scene before me and let it pervade my very being, but my intrusive thoughts about having eaten too much and too late continued. I'd have to work a little harder to completely silence that nasty little voice in my head. So, I wrote down everything I had eaten that day. I reviewed the list and told myself, "I am not fat. I eat a well-balanced diet and exercise regularly." Then I wrote five positive statements about myself, took a few deep breaths in and out, and rejoined my friends inside. Once again, I proved to myself that the pen was, indeed, mightier than the disorder.

Other Tools to Recovery

Perhaps the most regular warning sign I experience prior to feeling the urge to binge is a general sense of "antsyness", like I

65

can't sit still or concentrate on anything. Sometimes it's physiological, like butterflies in my stomach, and other times it's just an awareness that I'm thinking about food and can't seem to stop thinking about it. If I'm in tune with those feelings and thoughts or recognize that I'm in danger of bingeing, I can grab my pen and start writing, searching for reasons why I might be stressed. But sometimes, the urge to binge creeps up on me unnoticed for some time until I suddenly realize I'm pacing around the kitchen like a wildcat on the prowl for its next kill. During those instances, when I find myself standing in front of the open refrigerator door or with my hand halfway inside a bag of chips, writing doesn't always have the immediate impact I need. So, I will be forever grateful for prayer, my toothbrush and dental floss, my phone, and my body.

Although I practically grew up in a church, I haven't always been aware of God's presence in my life. I went through periods of doubt and disbelief, especially during the year before and after my divorce. Thankfully, God revealed himself to me anew through my lifelong love of singing and with that revelation came a rediscovery of the benefits of prayer. As a child, I prayed out of duty, in order to obey my parents. My standard nighttime prayer was this: "Father in heaven, hear my prayer. Keep me in Thy loving care. Be my guide in all I do. Bless all those who love me, too. Amen." I often finished with a request for general blessings on every single member of my close and extended family, including our cats, Tinkerbell and Trapper, who I always named fourth and fifth on the list, just after my parents and my brother.

When I was in college, my prayers became more "mature"; I prayed for peace of mind and happiness during a tumultuous freshman year. I prayed for the safety of family and friends far away from me. And I prayed for guidance when overwhelmed by the challenges and new experiences of college life. Each prayer left me with a feeling of peace that "surpasses all understanding" (New Testament of the Bible; Philippians 4:7). So, it wasn't surprising to me when I recently rediscovered that praying to God is a wonderful way to divert my attention from that pre-binge ants-in-my-pants feeling and fill me with calm. Whether down on my knees with eyes closed or sitting on the couch looking out the window at the moon, I find immediate peace and comfort when talking to God through prayer. Most often my pre-binge prayers include admitting that I'm about to binge, telling God that I trust He can help me through this, and then praising Him for all the blessings he has already bestowed on me. That's my favorite part of each prayer, because once I start thanking God for the most obvious things in my life—caring friends, a loving family—it's hard not to recall the hundreds of other "good gifts" He's given. I thank Him for the beautiful Earth and all its creatures, the sun, the stars and the moon, music, love, forgiveness, a secure job, a place to live, and food on my table. From there, my thoughts often drift towards others and I ask God to help me find ways to reach out to those who don't have a home or loving family or job or food. Thus, prayer becomes a bit like the thought restructuring I mentioned earlier...my thoughts quickly go from inwardly directed and negative to outwardly directed and positive.

Before prayer became part of my daily life, brushing and flossing my teeth were top among my binge-avoiding tricks. The clean feeling in my mouth acts as a reminder of my commitment not to binge. Actually, at first I tried just brushing my teeth, but that wasn't enough of a deterrent. If I felt a really strong urge to binge, I'd think, "What the heck! You can always brush your teeth again later." So (to my dentist's delight), I introduced flossing as "double protection". You see, I absolutely hate flossing my teeth; it's a slow and gross process, all those food particles stuck to the floss and my fingers and flicked onto the mirror! I try to do it every night, but there's no way I'm going to do it twice in one night, so I find that if I brush and then floss my teeth immediately after my 8 o'clock dinner, I am less likely to succumb to any urges to binge.

In addition to the above tools, my phone has also helped me prevent a binge. When I got out of B.E.D. in 2004 that first time, I told some trusted people about my disorder in order to build up a support network that I could rely on when I needed help. My dad, who understood my struggles well, was an obvious addition to my team. My mom and my two best friends are also on the list. These four are a great line of defense when the urge to binge is really strong. Just the act of dialing one of these four people is calming in and of itself. At any troublesome moment, I know that there is someone willing to listen to me. That person doesn't have to have any advice. Just sharing my frustrations and struggles with another person who knows and loves me relieves some of the burden. It reminds me that many people are invested in my recovery. And more often than not, each person will remind me of the numerous small successes I've experienced during this journey, successes which I may have otherwise been blinded to while staring at the bright "FAILURE" sign flashing before me. As that sign fades out and the negative thoughts disappear, I suddenly have space in my head to "rent out" to whoever I'm talking to. I can say, "Thanks for helping me. Now tell me how *you* are," and then listen with the undivided attention I always want to devote to my loved ones.

Occasionally, if I don't turn to prayer, or my pen or toothbrush *and* none of my support team is available to talk, I use my body to resist bingeing. I stand up and stretch or go for a walk. Sometimes I do some of the deep-breathing exercises I learned years ago when I practiced yoga and Pilates. Then I pick out some "feel good music", turn up the volume and start moving. I dance around my living room like an excited child on Christmas Eve. Twirling my arms, marching in place, punching the air, and even just the act of moving around the room relieves some of the tension associated with avoiding a strong urge to binge. Sometimes I even imagine those negative thoughts are tangible objects (the sofa pillows work well) and I kick and punch at them until I'm doubled over in laughter and satisfied that those thoughts aren't coming back. Usually after a few minutes of physical activity, I also start to feel good about myself. I can say, "I really wanted to binge tonight but not only am I avoiding overeating, I'm actually doing something good for my body!" I'm then able to let go of the negative thoughts which were triggering my urge to binge.

Everything in my toolbox—prayer, my pen, my toothbrush and floss, my phone and my body—has worked effectively to help me avoid a binge. The best part about avoiding a binge is the feeling of triumph I get after the urge has subsided. However, as I said before, I don't always turn to my toolbox or my family for support. Occasionally I do give in to the urge to binge, due to fatigue or a temporary return of the negative automatic thoughts. Fortunately, in the aftermath of a binge these days, I'm able to remind myself that I'm a work in progress, a multi-faceted woman who is much more than simply what others see or what she thinks they see. These reminders are enough to keep me out of the binge cycle and prevent me from getting back in B.E.D. for an extended stay.

You, too, may have times when getting out of B.E.D. seems nearly impossible. If that happens, it may help to know that there are others out there who experience similar struggles.

Chapter Nine: Others Talk About Getting Out of B.E.D.

I mentioned early on in this book that I was surprised to learn that other acquaintances of mine knew what it was like to be caught in the binge cycle. I desperately wanted to hear their stories and once I did, I knew it would be important for me to share them with others. The following three stories were adapted from interviews I conducted between March and June 2006. The names presented here are pseudonyms: Karen, Robert, and Lydia.

I knew Karen through my job as a research assistant. During weekly meetings at which there was always food, I had heard her say things like, "Get the cookies away from me or I'll eat them all" and "No, thanks. I've eaten enough today." Her words were strikingly similar to my own, so I decided to find out her story…

Karen's Story

I was quite depressed as a child. I remember when I was about fourteen or fifteen and I would come home after school and eat and eat and eat. I'd go through bags and bags of chips and jars of cookies. My dad always bought groceries for the house, for everyone to share. So there would be this huge jar of cookies and I'd go in and eat the entire thing. Then I'd go and buy more cookies and put the jar back so that no one would notice. Soon it became a habit to stop by a provisions store every day after school and buy a whole lot of snack food. I'd go home and eat it all and then make sure it was cleared up before dinner.

I would always eat dinner even if I was completely stuffed. I would eat a huge full meal just so no one would get on my case. My dad knew that I was eating a lot. I put on a lot of weight. He would always give me a hard time about putting on weight. My sister was anorexic, so I think he was worried that I was going to have similar problems with my eating. I also think he was worried about aesthetics. When I was fifteen, he told me I'd be pretty if I lost fifteen kilos [about 30 pounds]. *That stuck in my head for the last ten years.*

So I kept bingeing in secret. We had those individually wrapped cheese slices and I would go down and get a couple slices, leave, and eat them. Then I'd go back down for more. I'm sure no one would have said anything if they saw me eating a slice of cheese, but I didn't want to get caught. I knew it was part of a bigger issue. I became afraid of getting caught, so I tried to avoid people. We had a housekeeper and I was always trying to make sure she was somewhere else when I was eating. At some point, though, I just got tired of always hiding and always being in secret.

In twelfth grade, after a horrific breakup with my boyfriend, I said to myself, "I'm starting over. I'm clearing out. I'm a new person." Looking back, this was probably a big part of breaking the binge cycle. I had a lot of negative energy, so I started windsurfing as a way to vent that. I started getting fitter and losing weight and that started me on a positive cycle.

Then I went to college. Coming to college, I knew that the first year is always rough, eating-wise. You hear stories of people gaining "the freshman fifteen". So I didn't let myself eat snack food or soda the entire year. Almost zero. 'Cause there's so much snack food around and I thought if I started eating even a little of it, I would just spiral out of control again. So, I didn't touch it. And it really helped. But it took me a while to relax away from that. In fact, I spent the next three years of college learning to eat a little bit of the foods I loved without being excessive. I remember freshman year how good it felt to not eat snacks at all. Being that in control was a big accomplishment. But now the times in my life when I've been able to have a little and stop myself are even more rewarding to me.

Sometimes I'll still wind up bingeing and I know I shouldn't but I'm able to forgive myself and that helps me not do it again. If I allow myself to feel bad [guilty] then I want to eat more to erase those negative feelings. The other day I caught myself going through a box of Wheat Thins like there was no tomorrow. Whenever I'm at my laptop working really hard on something, I get lost in thought. I eat without thinking about it. I try to avoid this by setting limits for myself ahead of time. I say, "Go, take something, and leave. That's it." Portioning things out ahead of time and not letting myself feel bad when I do binge have helped keep me out of that cycle.

I also try to exercise. That seems to help. And I still try to keep snack foods out of the house 'cause I know if there are bags of chips around I'll eat them. I've gotten to the point where I'm pretty confident that I won't always binge on that stuff, but I know it's a temptation. It's a holdover from freshman year when I just banned myself from snack foods altogether. I know that the easiest way to keep myself from bingeing is to not have it around at all. However, I try to mitigate that a little because, of course, the occasional snack isn't a bad thing. If I do slip up and binge, I try to tell myself, "I may binge once in a while but that doesn't make me a bad person" and "I'm not gonna balloon from one binge on ten cookies."

I think overcoming binge eating is a lifelong process. For me, it's mostly under control and I've gotten to the point where I really don't think of it as something to control, which is really where I want to be. But I know my history. I know in the back of my head that certain things are likely to trigger a binge. I've tried to build new habits, 'cause habits are hard to break. If you build good ones, you'll be stuck in a positive cycle.

*   *   *   *   *

Certain phrases in Karen's story may have brought to mind characteristics of Binge-Eating Disorder that I, my dad, or Amy mentioned previously. Bingeing in secret, buying replacement foods for things eaten, worrying about gaining weight during college, and avoiding certain foods are things the four of us seem to have in common. As you'll see with the next two stories as well, the main components of the binge cycle can be quite evident.

Robert was the next person to share a story with me. I knew him through another co-worker and we had met only once before we sat down to talk about our common struggles with bingeing. When I pulled into the parking lot of the ambulance company at which he was an E.M.T., I was quite excited. I honestly hadn't expected to find another man with B.E.D. who was willing to share his story with me. I wondered how similar his story would be to either mine or my dad's...

Robert's Story

As a kid, I was always taller and more thick-boned than others. Although I wasn't in any organized sports, I was very active, always running around. In high school I was starting to *gain weight. I wasn't morbidly obese, but overweight. When my parents were working through their divorce, I started eating more out of control. Food provided me with comfort and was a way to find some peace. I felt secure when I was physically full. In my late teens, I would eat whatever was in front of me no matter what the portion size was. I would fill a plate with food and just eat it until it was gone. There was nothing in moderation. I think that distorted my concept of being satisfied. Food was just a pleasurable event.*

Another thing that contributed to my overeating was Ritalin. In the late '80s I was diagnosed with A.D.D. [Attention-Deficit Disorder] and started taking Ritalin. I'm still taking it eighteen years later. One of the side effects is appetite suppression, so I'm not hungry when I need to be eating. When the drug wears off and I haven't eaten well, I'm suddenly hungry. And when the hunger hits me, I make poor food choices—easily accessible food that will fill me up fast. If I make too many small poor choices it turns into a big eating fest. I don't know why I do it. There's this feeling of being out of control.

I sometimes feel that loss of control even when I go out to a friend's place for dinner. They might serve me a piece of meat that I consider to be bigger than a serving size. That would be enough to trigger the loss of control over eating for the next couple hours. One part of me thinks, "So what? You just ate two servings of a piece of meat. It's not gonna kill you. Just don't eat so much later on." But the other part of me says, "Ha! You've just proven to yourself that you can't eat in moderation." That makes me feel like a failure, which makes me want to continue eating and even binge.

In the last couple of years, I've been diagnosed with non-insulin dependent diabetes, high blood pressure, and sleep apnea. All of those conditions are weight-related. Since I just turned thirty, I realized it's time to do something about it. I mean I was always big, but around December I broke the 300 pound mark. So I decided to join a fitness challenge through work. We had two teams of six people per team and the goal was to lose as much weight and gain as much muscle mass as we could in twelve weeks.

In the past I've been to nutritionists and they've shown me the food pyramid and told me what and when to eat. But I was working nights at the time and just trying to eat around my work schedule was very difficult. The more I would think about what I needed to eat and when my next meal was gonna be, the more obsessed I became. I would think about food non-stop. I would eat well until I would have a little splurge and then I'd think, "Oh man, this isn't working." Then I would give up and eat non-stop. So when we started this fitness challenge, I decided to go on Weight Watchers®. They have internet tools that will do all the point counting for you and tell you the point value of each food. You can also see a graph of your weight and find out how many points you should be eating to achieve your weight-loss goal. So, for twelve weeks, I just ate within the point range that they told me to and saw my physician regularly. Since January I've lost over fifty pounds.

But now I feel myself going back to old patterns of behavior. Sometimes I think the urge to binge is always gonna be there. I don't wanna gain back all the weight I took off. But feeling sad about it makes it seem okay to eat more, to use food for comfort like I did growing up. I think the only way I'm going to successfully avoid bingeing is to confront it and say, "All right. This is why you feel this way." Then eat in moderation and find something else to keep me busy.

You know, it's funny. As a full-time E.M.T., I have to make life and death decisions every day. That's the way it is. Some stranger calls me into his life during a medical emergency and I can just ask a few questions, figure out what's going on, what hospital to take him to, and then get him there. Yet making wise decisions about food is so difficult. The weight loss challenge has helped a lot. I'm still trying to determine what triggers the "out-of-control" feelings so I can work on avoiding a binge. But it feels good to know I've made it this far.

*   *   *   *   *

Lydia was much younger than the other people I had interviewed for the book. She sought me out after finding a newspaper article I wrote for my alma mater. While reading her first email to me, I was struck by her frankness; she wasn't at all afraid to admit her weaknesses and ask others for help. We exchanged several emails over the next few months and discovered the similarities in and differences between our admitted struggles. One sunny summer day, we met in a city park to talk in more detail…

Lydia's Story

When I was young, my parents always made it clear that "being fat is bad". One night during spring break in 8th grade, I was laying on my side on the bed reading a book and a little bit of my stomach hung over the side of my pants and my mom said, "Is that fat?!" I said, "I guess so." I felt like I had just been caught doing something wrong. She wanted me to start eating healthier, so I did. Before that I weighed 114 pounds. I lost about four pounds and then my mom said, "Oh you look great!" I thought, "What?! I only lost four pounds!" So I think that's why I started thinking that numbers were very important.

In 9th grade I started playing field hockey and with all that exercise, I dropped a few more pounds. When field hockey season ended, I started obsessing about gaining weight. Every little pound that went on I thought, "Oh my god! I'm getting fat!" My parents bought an elliptical machine and as spring break approached, I thought, "Okay. I'm not gonna be fat this year. I'm gonna get myself as skinny as I can get and then I'll look good in a bathing suit." I put ridiculous limits on my calorie amounts like 200 for breakfast, 200 for lunch, between 70 and 160 calories for snack and then 400 for dinner. By the time spring break came around I weighed 99 pounds and thought I looked great. But on spring break, I was so hungry that I binged like crazy. I ate anything I could. I gained five pounds. So I went right back to my old regimen of diet and exercise.

As soon as I got home from school each day, I would go on my elliptical and burn off exactly 100 calories and then I'd eat my little snack and then do a 45 minute workout or so. I was definitely hungry the whole time and felt weak and tired. In fact, that's how my bingeing started. I was so hungry all the time. I decided to have a splurge day. I thought, "Okay. I'll just let myself have whatever I want on Sundays and then I'll have something to look forward to throughout the week." Every Sunday I ate anything and everything. I estimated calorie counts between four and five thousand. Come Monday I thought, "Okay, a new week is beginning and I can go back on my diet."

By May of that year, I was 95 pounds. I never really had any weight goal in mind. I just kept dropping pounds and it felt good. It was like an obsession. It was a thing to do. Like a way to test my limits. And the bingeing continued as a weekly thing. But by the end of May my parents threatened to send me to a clinic. I finally got to the point where I thought, "This is ridiculous. I can't do this anymore. It's exhausting." I decided to just be good to myself during the summer. So for a few days I ate when I was hungry and stopped when I was full. I didn't gain a lot of weight at first. Gradually over the summer I went up to 100 but I thought "This is good. I like this. This way I'm not fat. If I stay at 100 like this, life will be great!" I went online to try to figure out how many calories I could eat each day in order to maintain my weight. And I figured it was about 1700-1800 calories. So I usually stuck to 1700. I would have 1600 on days when I didn't exercise. That seemed to work, but there would be days when I'd get really hungry because I wasn't spacing out my food well enough. So then I'd binge and beat myself up for it but I didn't really know any other way. It seemed like I was hungry all the time, so I thought if I actually listened to my body and ate when I was hungry, I'd eat all the time and get fat.

I started my junior year of high school at 5'3" and 110 pounds and I thought that was fat. My mom said I was starting to look better but I didn't care. For me it was always the number 100. I started restricting again, which left me feeling hungry and more vulnerable to a binge. Halloween of that year, I binged like no other (telling myself that everyone does on Halloween), but I just felt so horrible about it that it convinced me to stop. The guilt was tremendous. Having often turned to food in times of stress (in 10th grade, I'd have a carton of "Cookies and Cream" ice cream out on the desk when I had a difficult essay to write), it suddenly occurred to me that if I wanted to minimize stress, I couldn't have the guilt of bingeing hovering above me. Then I saw this National Eating Disorders Association ad which said something like, "Eat what you want when you're truly hungry. Stop when you're full. Do this instead of any diet and you're unlikely to ever have a weight problem or any eating disorder." I cut that out and put it on my mirror. That helped me walk away, breathe, and learn to eat only when I actually felt hungry.

At the same time, I discovered that if I ate a peanut butter sandwich for breakfast, I could remain full for really long periods of time. So I'd eat one at 7:30am and then be full until about 5pm. I think that's how I lost 12 pounds. When I was down to 98 again I thought, "Oh wow. This is really great!" What ultimately scared me out of the restricting calories thing was this book I read late in senior year called "Wasted" by Marya Hornbacher[11]. It's her story about being both bulimic and anorexic. I think reading it almost prompted more binges because I knew I was really thin. I allowed myself to eat whatever I wanted during lunch at school and binged more often. By the end of senior year I weighed 110 again.

When I went to college I thought, "I'm not gonna binge in college because I just won't keep as much food in my room and I'll be okay." But my roommate had a lot of food and she would rarely eat it. I also knew that she ate small amounts in the dining hall. That was definitely a trigger for me. I thought, "Why can't I eat that little?!" I'd feel bad about anything I ate. One time, she had one of those re-sealable bags of mini Oreos and I just ate the whole thing and then thought, "Oh my god this is horrible". The fact that she wasn't eating anything and I was eating my food and hers made me feel worse about myself.

On my birthday, just a few weeks into my freshman year, my mom and dad bought me this chocolate cake from the dining hall. I invited the whole floor of my dorm and gave away a lot of it but there was still a lot left over and I ate it all in one sitting. My binge days were more frequent than they had been in high school. That's when I started admitting I had a problem with binge eating. It's this complete loss of control...I don't know how to close the bag of chips, put it out of my sight and not think about it. Even when I'm not eating I keep thinking about it. "If I don't finish this, it's gonna stay on my mind. I might as well just finish it and get it off my mind." I'd open a sleeve of Pop-Tarts and eat one of them and try to put the other in a plastic bag for later, but very rarely did that work. Then I'd think, "Oh well, I ate two. I might as well just eat the whole box and get it out of my sight." I had this all or

---

[11] Hornbacher, Marya. (1998). *Wasted: A Memoir of Anorexia and Bulimia*. New York: HarperCollins Publishers, Inc.

nothing mentality where you eat the one thing and then you've gotta eat all of it to get it off your mind.

My bingeing continued to spin out of control freshman year and my weight continued to increase. But for some reason, everything just stopped at 132 pounds. I guess I just reached the point where what I was eating on a day to day basis was what my body needed and could handle. Also, at the end of the first semester, I rearranged my dorm room. The new arrangement was in such a way that my roommate's food was under her bed, out of sight, and my food was under mine. Mentally, it registered that what was under her bed was hers alone, and after that I never ate one piece of what she had. I kept less food in the plastic tub under my bed—just rice cakes to snack on and some breakfast foods; this decreased my urge to binge late at night. In addition, I started seeing a therapist at school and after each session, I always felt good about myself. She even got me thinking that I could one day help people with eating disorders like she does. Now that I'm home for the summer, there are times when I've had to say to my mom, "I can't have this food in the house. I feel really bad, but you're gonna have to throw it away or give it to the birds because I can't have this around."

Another thing that helped me break out of bingeing is that I don't weigh myself every day anymore. In January of my senior year of high school, I started keeping track of my weight every day, but the number on the scale dictated my mood for the day and how I perceived myself. So, I stopped weighing myself as often. In the last few months I decided to start focusing on the positives about myself. Like the fact that girls are supposed to have curves and I now have curves!

I also don't count calories anymore. That was a huge step. Through a very gradual process, I have finally learned to just eat when I'm hungry and stop when I'm full. I bought a pack of 12oz bottles of (non-diet) soda, but I rarely go through a whole bottle. I just listen to my body and when I'm full, I dump the rest down the drain. So what if I'm wasting a little bit of money? I'd rather do that than feel horrible. I now feel comfortable with what I eat. It feels great to order what I want at a restaurant rather than what I feel I should order.

*　　　*　　　*　　　*　　　*

78

The preceding stories are quite different from one another in terms of the development and the details of each person's relationship with food. If there's one simple truth to be learned from reading the stories in this book, it's that eating disorders are rarely caused by a single factor. Recalling Amy's story from the beginning of the book, it began with a change in her self-concept from "skinny girl" to "fat person", as well as introduction to an environment of easily accessible food. In Karen's case it was a combination of several things: childhood depression, a sister with an eating disorder, and again, the availability of food. Robert's adult eating habits may have been influenced by his childhood perception of his physical body and the positive feedback he felt when eating to relieve tension. Lydia's parents' mixed messages about what it means to be attractive may have contributed to her anorexia, while her subsequent awareness that she was underweight preceded her difficulties with binge eating.

Despite the varied life experiences that can contribute to the development of Binge-Eating Disorder, we've seen here that there are many common characteristics exhibited by those who are caught in the binge cycle. For example, Amy, Karen, Robert, and Lydia each talk of feeling as though they had lost all control over their eating or could lose control at any moment:

Amy: "I know I can't control myself around certain foods so I can't have them in the house."

Karen: "I thought if I started eating even a little [snack food], I would just spiral out of control again. So, I didn't touch it."

Robert: "If I make too many small poor choices it turns into a big eating fest. I don't know why I do it. There's this feeling of being out of control."

Lydia: "It's this complete loss of control...I don't know how to close the bag of chips, put it out of my sight and not think about it. Even when I'm not eating I keep thinking about it."

This feeling of being out of control of one's eating is one of the hallmarks of Binge-Eating Disorder, as is a feeling of disgust, guilt, failure or self-loathing after a period of overeating:

Amy: "I would have one and then I'd have to have another and another until I ate so much of it that I felt horrible about myself."

Karen: "Sometimes I'll still wind up bingeing and I know I shouldn't but I'm able to forgive myself and that helps me not do it again. If I allow myself to feel bad [*guilty*] then I want to eat more to erase those negative feelings."

Robert: "[If I eat something] I consider to be bigger than a serving size...that would be enough to trigger the loss of control over eating for the next couple hours...That makes me feel like a failure, which makes me want to continue eating and even binge."

Lydia: "[In college], I'd feel bad about *anything* I ate. One time, [my roommate] had one of those re-sealable bags of mini Oreos and I just ate the whole thing and then thought, 'Oh my god this is horrible'."

All four individuals experienced the pain of self-loathing at some point, yet perhaps most inspiring about all these stories is that each person was willing to venture away from B.E.D. in the hope of breaking the chains that held them there. I'm sure any of us who have gotten out of B.E.D. even just once will attest to the wonderful feeling of freedom that comes from consuming food without letting food consume us. You and your loved ones can also experience this freedom. If you're unsure how to start, read on for a review of some of the techniques recommended by eating disorder experts.

"For everything there is a season,
and a time for every matter under heaven…
a time to break down, and a time to build up;
a time to weep, and a time to laugh…"

--from the Bible: Ecclesiastes 3:1,3-4

By this point in our journey, you may recognize in yourself some of the thoughts, emotions, and behaviors described thus far. You may be thinking, "*Now* is my 'time to break down' the old habits and 'build up' my toolbox!" Yet, it can be overwhelming and nerve-wracking to contemplate what life will be like outside the confines of the binge cycle. Let me assure you that these feelings are natural and will pass the more times you do get out of B.E.D.—even if it's just for a few moments. Allow yourself to consider the possibilities: no more intrusive thoughts about what you look like or weigh, no more counting calories and creating unrealistic diet plans, no more bingeing and self-loathing. You could even feel an increase in your self-esteem and confidence. Imagine how much time would be left in the day to do things with your family, help others, pursue old or discover new interests, or just enjoy life as it unfolds before you.

These are just a few of the benefits I've found from getting out of B.E.D. Today, over three years into my recovery, just knowing how much I've gained by overcoming binge eating (self-confidence, inner strength, peace of mind) is motivation enough for me to continue trying to do so as often as I can. If you are ready to throw off your own covers and get out of B.E.D., but don't know where to begin, here is some insight through two books written by eating disorders experts.

Keeping a Food Journal

Two self-help books were instrumental in my recovery from Binge-Eating Disorder. Both of these books list "self-monitoring" among the first steps to overcoming binge eating. Dr. Joyce D. Nash says that self-monitoring involves "keeping a record of when, where, and what you eat, the circumstances that contributed to the eating behavior, whether it was a binge, and your thoughts and feelings at each step of the way. "[12]

Taking note of what you eat and when, in addition to how you feel physically and emotionally when eating may help you find patterns within your eating habits and uncover situations or stressors that consistently trigger a binge. Sound like a daunting and undesirable task? Dr. Christopher G. Fairburn writes, "You may say that you are all too aware of the problem. In a sense, of course, this is true. But accurate monitoring almost always highlights features that were not obvious beforehand."[13]

As mentioned in Chapter 5, I kept a food journal and found it to be both revealing and empowering. Just knowing what emotional states and ˙situations triggered my binges (boredom, loneliness, too much work, etc.) gave me the drive to push those suffocating covers off me and find other ways to deal with the tension. I knew that anything was better than the constant emotional tug-of-war in which I felt okay about myself one minute and hated myself the next.

---

[12] Nash, Joyce D. (1999). *Binge No More: Your Guide to Overcoming Disordered Eating*. Oakland: New Harbinger Publications, Inc. p. 111 (Reprinted by permission).
[13] Fairburn, Dr. Christopher G. (1995). *Overcoming Binge Eating*. New York: Guilford Press. p. 145 (Reprinted by permission).

Food Journal Entry: Sunday, August 15, 2004

Time	Food/Drink	Place	Comments
11:40	½ a turkey, cheese & tomato sandwich; 2 bites potato salad; 1 serving veggie chips; cup of coffee w/ sugar	living rm.	woke up late so I skipped breakfast
3:50	apple w/ 1 Tbsp peanut butter	living rm.	felt good about the amount of time btw lunch and now
7:00	salad w/ balsamic drsg; chicken & mushroom pie; a rum & pineapple juice; ½ piece of key lime pie	restaurant	feel nervous about having both a drink & a dessert
9:00	8oz soda	theatre	had that "why not" feeling
11:45	cup of tea w/ milk & sugar	living rm.	needed something to calm my nerves; still nervous about dinner

This is just one way to self-monitor. Self-help books may recommend keeping track of slightly different information, but the goal is the same: keep track for a few weeks, review your entries and discover what emotional states and situations trigger your binges (or urges to binge). In my entry above, I didn't succumb to a binge, but I was definitely on the verge of one, having noted feelings of guilt, a belief that I had eaten "too much" that day and a desire to just eat whatever I wanted the rest of the day. Although it is certainly not easy or fun to do so, writing and reviewing my food journal entries was immensely helpful to me.

However, not everyone with Binge-Eating Disorder finds keeping a food journal helpful or even possible. In fact, Lydia had this to say about journaling:

I bought this book senior year that recommends keeping a food journal every day about how hungry you are, what you eat, and what you're feeling at the time. I did that for about two weeks but then it just got aggravating. I couldn't do it. Journaling for me was just so much work. I didn't have time for it on top of all my homework.

You, too, may feel that you are too busy to make time to write down everything you eat and how you felt when you ate it. Or maybe you already keep a mental list of what you eat each day and feel that you don't need or want to actually write it all down on paper. I, too, was incredibly adept at remembering exactly what and how much I ate. Yet, it wasn't until I took note of the feelings I had before, during, and after each meal or snack that I began to understand the strong link between my emotions and my eating habits.

So, although it may be difficult at first, try keeping a journal like mine or design one of your own. After two weeks, review your entries. Are there patterns to your eating? Are your meals spaced too far apart, leaving you feeling starved and thus more prone to binge? Do you feel guilty about eating particular foods or certain quantities of food? Do you eat more at certain times of the day? Answering these questions allowed me to make the first move forward.

Which Weigh to the Scale?

An equally important part of self-monitoring is weighing. Some of you may have become a slave to the scale, like I have been. Others of you may avoid the scale altogether. In *Binge No More*, Dr. Nash says, "it is best to weigh yourself only once a week. Choose the same day and the same time of day."[14] Dr. Fairburn has similar advice in *Overcoming Binge Eating*: "...it is highly likely that your eating habits will change. It is therefore appropriate that you monitor your weight. The best way of doing this is to weigh yourself once a week."[15] Many of us with disordered eating are preoccupied with our weight. Not weighing at all doesn't necessarily decrease our "weight woes" and

---

[14] Nash, Joyce D. (1999). *Binge No More: Your Guide to Overcoming Disordered Eating*. Oakland: New Harbinger Publications, Inc. p. 126 (Reprinted by permission).

[15] Fairburn, Dr. Christopher G. (1995). *Overcoming Binge Eating*. New York: Guilford Press. p. 150 (Reprinted by permission).

obsessively weighing every day or multiple times a day can lead to feelings of self-loathing every time the number increases. Dr. Fairburn says, "to identify changes in your weight, don't rely too heavily on individual readings since body weight fluctuates from day to day. Single readings can therefore be misleading. Instead, look for trends over several weeks (three or four readings) since only in this way can you detect true changes."[16]

Having kept track of my weight daily for many years and obsessed over every little increase, this weekly weigh-in plan sounded like a good idea for my own recovery. In July of 2004, I cut back from weighing myself daily to just weekly. During week four, I weighed almost the same as week one, thus I had "proof" that I was not gaining weight. However, over a year later, I was still greatly concerned with the number on the scale. It still influenced how I felt about myself and what kinds of foods I ate during the next week.

It wasn't until I read the following, from a terrific book by Jenni Schaefer, a young woman who overcame both anorexia and bulimia, that I decided to prohibit myself from daily weigh-ins:

"When I began recovery, I quickly called it quits with the scale...in addition to giving up the scale, I decided that I no longer wanted anyone to tell me my weight. I would let the doctor weigh me only with the understanding that I did not want to know the number."[17]

I hadn't even considered the possibility of not weighing. After all, how would I be able to evaluate my self-worth if I didn't know how much I weighed? The truth is that I would be forced to define myself by something other than weight. I knew that would be the true test of my recovery. I had been able to get out of B.E.D. many times, more often than not, yet I was still concerned about my body image and weight.

---

[16] Fairburn, Dr. Christopher G. (1995). *Overcoming Binge Eating*. New York: Guilford Press. p. 150 (Reprinted by permission).
[17] Schaefer, Jenni with Rutledge, Thom. (2004). *Life Without Ed: How One Woman Declared Independence from Her Eating Disorder and How You Can Too*. New York: McGraw-Hill. p. 66. (Material reproduced by permission of The McGraw-Hill Companies).

Jenni's decision to not weigh herself seemed to be a good "next step" for me at that moment in time. On January 9, 2006, I weighed myself for what I thought would be the last time. At that time I weighed 152 pounds and had no idea how much weight I'd gain or lose before I next got on the scale. Don't get me wrong—abandoning the scale wasn't easy, especially since my boyfriend's relationship with the scale wasn't over, so throwing it away altogether wasn't an option. There are days when I would see it sitting next to our bathroom sink and have a strong and sudden urge to "just find out. What harm will that do?" But I kept forbidding myself to do so because I knew that not knowing that little number would open my eyes to many of my previously ignored skills, talents, and attributes. For a while, I not only didn't weigh myself at home, but I also didn't allow my doctors to tell me my weight, just as Jenni Schaefer had done. Each visit to the doctor, I said to the nurse, as I stepped on the scale, "I'm trying to overcome an eating disorder. Part of my recovery involves not weighing myself anymore, so I'll just turn around while you weigh me and if you don't mind, just write the number in my chart rather than say it out loud. Thank you." The first time I said that I was shaking with nervousness, but the nurse didn't seem to mind and I knew that my recovery was my business. I had to do whatever I could to stay on track.

Some of you may find peace of mind from weighing yourself weekly. At that point in my recovery, I wanted to prove to myself that I was no longer a slave to my scale. I went for 14 months without weighing myself. Then one morning in early April I overheard my inner critic taunting, "Go on. Get on the scale. It's been forever. Just find out what you weigh and then don't get on it again." Perhaps because it was first thing in the morning and my gentler, wiser self hadn't yet "woken up", I agreed with my critic and stepped on the scale, heart pounding because something inside me knew this was a bad idea. A new voice started screaming in my head: "Don't do it! Don't ruin it! You don't have to know!" In an attempt to stifle the voice, I mumbled some positive words under my breath, "I am not a number. I am Megan Rachel Bartlett!", and looked down. I couldn't believe what I saw. The number "152" glared up at me in red neon. I weighed the exact same thing I had weighed 14 months earlier. My inner critic was giddy with happiness: "Good job, Megan! You didn't gain any weight!" I felt like a million bucks that day. I continued to weigh myself every

Saturday morning for six weeks. Soon, though, I felt myself sliding backwards down a slippery slope, right back to where I had started—a slave to the scale. I discovered it on a Thursday afternoon when I heard my critic saying, "Whoa! You've been eating a lot of junk food this week. You better slow down for the next 48 hours or you might weigh more this Saturday than you did last week."

The realization of my re-enslavement was quite a blow and my critic found plenty of ways to berate me: "Aren't you over this yet? What was all your hard work for? Why are you writing a book about your recovery if you're not even recovered yet?" Fortunately, I knew I could and *must* put him in his place: "Listen up! I am a work in progress. I'm doing the best I can. I had a small set-back, but it's not the end of the world. I am still Megan Rachel Bartlett and I'm going to learn from this set-back and simply re-dedicate myself to NOT weighing anymore." What a relief! It felt great to have the strength within me to say that. And what an important lesson for me to learn: recovery is an ongoing process and one which may include set-backs. Set-backs are not failures. They're just opportunities to learn and try again.

During your recovery, you'll also have many opportunities to learn from your experiences. You may try some things that I or other authors recommend and find them totally unhelpful to you. That's okay. It's just important to keep trying. I still recommend self-monitoring through journaling (and weekly weighing if you feel comfortable doing so) as your first steps in overcoming binge eating. Then you'll be ready to move on to the next step: establishing a more regular eating schedule.

Eating More to Eat Less

If you're concerned about your weight and body shape and you frequently binge eat, it may seem counter-intuitive, even crazy, when I tell you that I had to eat more in order to ultimately eat less. Whenever I finished a binge, I vowed to restrict my calories in order to make up for it. I'd try to eat as little as possible (or even just eat "moderately") but either physical hunger or stress would creep up on me and I'd grab a "quick fix" snack. Quick fix foods are often more caloric, less nutritious, and less satisfying than a pre-planned snack might be. If you're reaching for a quick fix food during a state of intense physical hunger, as I often was on restriction days, you may find yourself consuming many things in a short period of time in an attempt to satiate that hungry feeling, which can take a while to subside. In accordance with Dr. Fairburn's and Dr. Nash's advice, I decided to eat more in order to eat less; I established a regular pattern of three meals a day and a few planned snacks with the expectation that I would eventually feel less of an urge to binge.[18,19] My first attempt at an eating plan looked like this:

8:00am – breakfast
10:00am – mid-morning snack
12:30pm – lunch
3:00pm – mid-afternoon snack
6:30pm – early evening snack
8:30pm – dinner

Many people find that eating every few hours satisfies their food cravings and feelings of physical hunger. I discovered that eating every 2 to 2 ½ hours was too often for me. I wasn't feeling hungry enough and thus felt that I was eating excessively. I wrote a new plan, eating slightly more at each meal/snack but only eating every four hours. This seemed to be the right rhythm for my body, so I stuck with it, although at this point in my recovery I do allow for deviations from this plan:

8:00am – breakfast
12:00pm – lunch
4:00pm – afternoon snack
8:00pm – dinner

Only you will know what eating schedule will be best for you. Try eating every three hours and see how that goes. If that doesn't work, try a different routine. It's important to be both persistent in your efforts to get out of B.E.D. (think about how difficult it is to drag yourself out from under the warm covers of your literal bed on a cold winter morning) and flexible with your eating schedule. We all know there are some days when we just feel hungrier than

---

[18] Fairburn, Christopher G. (1995). *Overcoming Binge Eating*. New York: Guilford Press. p. 157 (Reprinted by permission).
[19] Nash, Joyce D. (1999). *Binge No More: Your Guide to Overcoming Disordered Eating*. Oakland: New Harbinger Publications, Inc. p. 137 (Reprinted by permission).

other days. On those days, you may want to allow yourself to add another snack. There will also be times when you are offered food at a point in the day when you're not "scheduled" for a meal or a snack. If you feel "safe" enough to deviate from your schedule and have some, go ahead. You can always readjust your meal plan for that day by eating a smaller amount at the next scheduled time or choosing healthful foods as part of your next meal. As someone who tried a few different eating schedules, I can say that just establishing and following an eating routine drastically reduced the frequency of my binges.

Finding Alternatives to Bingeing

"So," you ask, "what do I do when I still feel the urge to binge even after keeping a food journal, finding patterns in my eating habits, and establishing a regular eating routine?" Well, I followed the advice of Dr. Fairburn: "construct a list of alternative activities"[20] to turn to when the urge to binge is strong. Although this may seem like simply diverting your attention from the real issue, it's an effective tool to stop bingeing. (And boy, does it feel great when you successfully avoid a binge!) As I mentioned in Chapter 5, having this list at the ready was incredibly helpful to me. My original list included thirteen different activities, but after some trial and error, I regularly turned to just five of them. Later, I added a few more (see Chapter 8).

Take a few minutes right now to make a list of possible things to do when *you* feel the urge to binge. Keep in mind that some of the best binge-preventing activities are those that are 1) emotionally and mentally absorbing (a few of my favorites are praying, reading the bible, or writing) or 2) far away from food (I like to go for a walk or a drive or go shopping—anything but food shopping!). There may, of course, be alternative activities that don't work, like the time I left my apartment in order to get away from the food in my kitchen and ended up walking to a convenience store and buying two snacks! Don't get discouraged. It took me several months to find five reliable, useful substitutions for bingeing. You can do it. And when you do, you'll have successfully gotten out of B.E.D. for the first time!

---

[20] Fairburn, Dr. Christopher G. (1995). *Overcoming Binge Eating*. New York: Guilford Press. p. 172 (Reprinted by permission).

It is difficult for me to say exactly which steps that I have taken were the most effective; I have benefited in some way from each of the techniques I've mentioned here. Yet, I feel strongly that I would not have been able to walk away from my B.E.D. day after day after day if I hadn't spent a significant amount of time contradicting my inner critic. The daily task of challenging my negative automatic thoughts was (and continues to be) one of the most difficult.

In *Binge No More*, Dr. Nash says, "how you understand an event or a situation influences how you feel about it."[21] I've found this to be an undeniable truth which can be either devastating or comforting. There are still days when I hear my inner critic warn, "You've been eating too much lately. You better cut back or you'll get fat." and I am at a loss for what to say in response. It seems like sound advice, so I find it easy to agree with the thoughts. I think, "Yes, I have been eating more. I must be getting fat. People will notice my fat and think I'm disgusting. If they think I'm disgusting I'll be worthless." The thoughts can quickly turn into feelings of self-loathing. But I know if I allow myself to feel miserable and self-conscious, I'll be tempted to crawl back in B.E.D. Knowing how great it feels to not hate myself, I strive to not fall into that cycle by stopping negative thoughts as soon as they occur. Sometimes all it takes is a single positive statement to get me feeling better about myself. Other times it takes a more concentrated effort.

Countering negative thoughts with positive ones may be your greatest challenge, too. You may want to do as my counselor recommended to me: "learn to recognize and listen to your self-talk". When you're aware of it, you may want to write down some of the negative thoughts and try to come up with positive, self-affirming responses to them. At first you may only hear negative, food-related talk. After a while, however, you may find that your inner critic oversees many different areas of your life: your self-worth, your abilities, and even your desires. Here are several of my recent attempts to counter negative self-talk:

---

[21] Nash, Joyce D. *Binge No More: Your Guide to Overcoming Disordered Eating*. Oakland: New Harbinger Publications, Inc. p.150 (Reprinted by permission).

Negative Thought	Positive Statement
1. I'm so fat.	I'm not fat. I eat a well-balanced diet that now includes foods I once feared. I exercise regularly and feel better than I've felt in years.
2. There's no way I can stop bingeing.	I can stop and I will. I just have to take it one day at a time.
3. People will like me better if I'm thin.	People already like me. They also appreciate me in each of my roles: daughter, sister, co-worker, friend.
4. I'm paying way too much attention to myself these days!	I like helping other people. In order to be a most effective "helper", I need to spend time helping myself first.
5. I'm too reliant on my self-help tools.	If I have to go through life with 'crutches', so be it. At least I have them.

As you go through the next few days, try to listen for those automatic thoughts. You'll know they're automatic because they pop up quickly and linger for quite a while, often with devastating consequences. For me, these kinds of thoughts take on a physical shape not unlike a little red cartoon devil perched on my left shoulder. If I haven't been keeping up with my positive counter-statements, I can see him bright as ever (much like the red neon "FAILURE" sign), while the loving angel on my right fades away until he's nearly invisible. The great thing about finally noticing your negative thoughts is that you can then do something about them.

So, go ahead and start pumping yourself full of positive, self-affirming thoughts. Tell your inner critic to take a hike! Peace of mind, happiness, increased self-esteem, and renewed interest in life are just a few of the benefits of getting out of B.E.D. I sincerely hope that the stories and insights I have shared will be encouraging to you in your daily choice to get out of B.E.D.

Epilogue: Life Anew

Throughout my childhood, adolescence and adulthood, I have enjoyed creative writing and poetry. Getting out of B.E.D. freed me from the constant internal monologue of intrusive negative thoughts and enabled me to spend more time on activities I enjoy like writing. One evening, a few months into my recovery, I wrote a haiku to express my joy about having finally seen a glimpse of the beautiful person inside me:

> Cautiously at first,
> the butterfly emerges
> to face life anew.

As the poem suggests, emerging from my seemingly comfortable cocoon was scary, but I did it. I was finally able to shed the old me and celebrate the new.

As chef Nigella Lawson says, "In order to celebrate the pleasure of being alive, you need food: the very symbol of life, and what sustains it." [22] I hope that you, too, recognize the strength within you to emerge from within your cocoon and fly away from the confines of your B.E.D. with renewed hope, inner peace, and the ability to eat food in celebration of your beautiful and unique life.

---

[22] Lawson, Nigella (2004). *Feast: Food That Celebrates Life.* New York: Hyperion. p.318 (Reprinted by permission).

Suggested Websites and Readings for Further Information

Websites

The following is a brief list of online resources that provide important information for those with Binge-Eating Disorder or simply present the information in a unique way. Keep in mind that there are thousands of websites that mention, define, or discuss Binge-Eating Disorder. These are just five of the most comprehensive ones I have found.

1. National Eating Disorders Association (NEDA) - www.nationaleatingdisorders.org

> NEDA is a non-profit organization in the United States aimed at preventing eating disorders and providing treatment referrals for them. Their website includes information about specific eating disorders, as well as programs sponsored by NEDA and ways to get involved in eating disorders awareness and prevention.

2. Weight-control Information Network (WIN) - http://win.niddk.nih.gov/publications/binge.htm#moreinfo

> WIN is a service of the National Institute of Diabetes and Digestive and Kidney Diseases. The website provides information about Binge-Eating Disorder and a nice list of treatment programs for those diagnosed with the disorder.

3. Something Fishy - www.something-fishy.org

> Something Fishy is a website dedicated to raising awareness and providing support to people with eating disorders and their loved ones. The site emphasizes the idea that eating disorders are symptoms of deeper unresolved issues such as depression, low self-esteem, fears, etc. The site contains everything from general information and treatment resources to a poetry corner and online recovery games.

4. At Health, Inc. -
http://www.athealth.com/consumer/disorders/bingeeating.html

> At Health, Inc. is a mental health information network for both laypeople and professionals. The website is not dedicated to Binge-Eating Disorder, but it does have a nice page of easy-to-understand information, links to treatment centers and therapists, and an online bookstore.

5. BEAT – Beating Eating Disorders - http://www.b-eat.co.uk

> BEAT™ is a charitable organization in the United Kingdom. The website provides some helpful advice for young people who know someone with an eating disorder, as well as a Q&A section for adults. There are also message boards and chat rooms to which people with eating disorders can contribute stories or ask questions.

Books/Publications

The following is by no means a comprehensive list of books and publications on the subject of Binge-Eating Disorder. These are many of the ones I have found most helpful in my recovery or believe will be helpful to others.

<u>Self-help books</u>

1. Burris, Kelly (2004). *Reprogramming the Overweight Mind: 7 Steps to Taking Control of Your Subconscious.* Illumine Studios.

2. Danowski, Debbie and Lazaro, Pedro. (2000). *Why Can't I Stop Eating?: Recognizing, Understanding, and Overcoming Food Addiction.* Center City, Minnesota: Hazelden.

3. Danowski, Debbie (2004). *The Overeater's Journal: Exercises for the Heart, Mind and Soul.* Center City, Minnesota: Hazelden.

4. Fairburn, Dr. Christopher G. (1995). *Overcoming Binge Eating.* New York: Guilford Press.

5. Hirschmann, Jane R. and Munter, Carol H. (1998). *Overcoming Overeating.* New York: Fawcett Crest.

6. Migliore, Marilyn. (1998). *The Hunger Within: A Twelve Week Guided Journey from Compulsive Eating to Recovery.* New York: Main Street Books.

7. Nash, Joyce D. (1999). *Binge No More: Your Guide to Overcoming Disordered Eating.* Oakland: New Harbinger Publications, Inc.

8. Pfeiffer, Richard H. (1998). *The Real Solution Binge/ Compulsive Eating Workbook.* New York: Growth Publishing.

9. Schmidt, Ulrike. (1993). *Getting Better Bit(e) by Bit(e): A Survival Kit for Sufferers of Bulimia and Binge Eating Disorders.* East Sussex, United Kingdom: Psychology Press Ltd.

Guides for Families/Friends

1. Albronda Heaton, Jeanne and Strauss, Claudia J. (2005). *Talking to Eating Disorders: Simple Ways to Support Someone With Anorexia, Bulimia, Binge Eating, Or Body Image Issues.* New York: Penguin Group, Inc.

2. Moraghan Jablow, Martha and Kopp, C. Everett. (1991). *A Parent's Guide to Eating Disorders and Obesity (The Children's Hospital of Philadelphia Series).* New York: Dell Publishing.

3. Natenshon, Abigail H. (1999). *When Your Child Has an Eating Disorder: A Step-by-Step Workbook for Parents and Other Caregivers.* San Francisco: Jossey-Bass, Inc.

4. Siegel, Michele, Brisman, Judith, and Weinshel, Margot. (1997). *Surviving an Eating Disorder: Strategies for Families and Friends.* New York: Harper Collins Publishers, Inc.

Biographies/Memoirs

1. Saxen, Ron. (2007). *The Good Eater.* Oakland: New Harbinger Publications, Inc.

2. Schaefer, Jenni with Rutledge, Thom. (2004). *Life Without Ed: How One Woman Declared Independence from Her Eating Disorder and How You Can Too.* New York: McGraw-Hill.

3. Thomas, Pattie with Wilkerson, Carl and Campos, Paul. (2005). *Taking Up Space: How Eating Well and Exercising Regularly Changed My Life.* Nashville: Pearlsong Press.

4. Watson, C.L. (2006). *Eating the Shadow: A Memoir of Loss and Recovery.* Stone Ridge: Fenn Books and Media.

Books about Writing as Therapy

1. Bolton, Gillie. (1998). *The Therapeutic Potential of Creative Writing: Writing Myself.* London: Jessica Kingsley Publishers.

2. Campbell, Andrea. (2000). *Your Corner of the Universe: A Guide to Self-Therapy through Journal Writing.* (2nd Edition). New York: ASJA Press.

3. DeSalvo, Louise (1999). Writing as a Way of Healing: How Telling Our Stories Transforms Our Lives. New York: HarperSanFrancisco.

4. Hunt, Celia and Sampson, Fiona. (1998). *The Self on the Page: Theory and Practice of Creative Writing in Personal Development.* London: Jessica Kingsley Publishers.

5. Klauser, Henriette Anne. (1995). *Put Your Heart on Paper.* New York: Bantam.

6. Philips, Deborah, Linington, Liz, Penman, Debra. (1999). *Writing Well: Creative Writing and Mental Health.* London: Jessica Kingsley Publishers.

Permissions Acknowledgments